Measuring Stratigraphic Sections

The Geologic Field Techniques Series was conceived in response to a need, repeatedly expressed by both students and practicing geologists, for a more comprehensive treatment of established techniques for conducting basic operations in the field. The volumes in this Series are deliberately focused upon field operations, and each is concerned with a single broad topic in this area. The use and interpretation of results is left to the several excellent publications that deal more generally with the study and understanding of geologic features. Because many field techniques can be widely applied, the present volumes may prove helpful not only to geologists but also to foresters, archeologists, engineers, and others for whom the laboratory is outdoors. The compact format of the books in the Series permits their use as ready reference in the field.

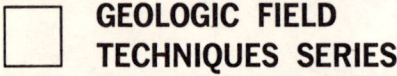

GEOLOGIC FIELD TECHNIQUES SERIES

Richard H. Jahns, Editor

Frank E. Kottlowski MEASURING STRATIGRAPHIC SECTIONS

Laurence H. Lattman and Richard G. Ray AERIAL PHOTOGRAPHS IN FIELD GEOLOGY

MEASURING STRATIGRAPHIC SECTIONS

Frank E. Kottlowski
New Mexico Institute of Mining and Technology

HOLT, RINEHART AND WINSTON
New York ☐ Chicago ☐ San Francisco
Toronto ☐ London

Copyright © 1965 by Holt, Rinehart and Winston, Inc.
All Rights Reserved
Library of Congress Catalog Card Number 65-10434

25025-0115

Printed in the United States of America

Editor's Foreword

Implicit here is the view that the task of the investigator will be made easier if he can draw upon the experience of others in planning his general approach to a project, in choosing the instruments and materials to be used, and in determining the best means for obtaining and recording data during the course of his work. To be sure, the quality of his final results will depend mainly upon his own industry and skill in observing, measuring, reckoning, and reasoning, which derive much more from personal ability and experience than from any book. But many different methods can be applied in typical field operations, and few individuals become sufficiently familiar with all of them to assess their respective advantages and shortcomings for each set of field conditions encountered. Toward the effective selection and use of basic techniques, therefore, the summed experiences of earlier workers can provide a valuable head start.

This book is concerned with a fundamental element of field activities, the measuring of sections in layered materials. It represents a searching review of past and present practices, which the author has fortified with first-hand knowledge developed from his own extensive field investigations. He discusses purposes and applications of measured sections, factors to be considered in selecting sites for measurements, and many uses for the data that can be obtained. Specific instruments and procedures for establishing horizontal and vertical control are outlined in detail, and their advantages and limitations are correlated with possible combinations of topographic and geologic conditions. Considerable attention also is given to the systematic description of measured units and to the organization of pertinent field and laboratory data. The volume is intended to serve both students and experienced investigators in a wide variety of situations.

RICHARD H. JAHNS
Consulting Editor

Preface

Measured and described sections of layered rocks or other natural materials are fundamentally useful in most geologic and related studies, whether their emphasis is on stratigraphy, subsurface correlation, areal geologic mapping and interpretation, paleontology, sedimentation, geologic structure, petrology, or sampling of many kinds. Most geologists have had little real opportunity in their training or professional experience to consider fully the questions of why, where, and how to measure sections. All too often they limit themselves to application of only a few of the many contrasting techniques pertinent to such work. This manual describes these field techniques concisely but comprehensively. The emphasis is on methods that are swift and instruments that are relatively simple but will yield reasonably accurate results.

In this field manual an attempt is made to answer the questions of why, where, and how, in that order. The chief purposes for measuring sections are enumerated in Chapter 1, and their application to stratigraphy, subsurface correlation, areal and structural geology, and sampling problems are stressed. The selection of sections to be measured and general field procedures are treated in Chapter 2.

Chapters 3, 4, and 5 deal with the methods and instruments used in section measuring, as well as the types of field problems encountered, their geometric solution, and errors to be avoided. The final chapter deals briefly with descriptions of measured units and the attendant association with measurements, emphasizing both observed lithic features and their interpretation. Reference tables are included in the appendix.

The subject of section measuring has been treated briefly in other texts and manuals that consider over-all descriptions of geologic field methods. These excellent summaries tend to stress one or another technique of measurement. Numerous short articles on various aspects, mostly trigonometric, have been helpful. The field experiences of the writer have influenced the recommendations of methods for measurement, the items to be described, and the descriptive terms suggested.

Much of this manual has stemmed from the writer's own field training by Charles F. Deiss, Eugene Callaghan, and Paul Dean Proctor; technical advice from Richard H. Jahns, Max E. Willard, Roy W. Foster, Samuel Thompson III, Robert A. Bieberman, and Ralph M. McGehee; administrative encouragement by Alvin J. Thompson; and editorial critique by Richard H. Jahns. Richard Jahns' editorial advice, deeply appreciated by the writer, bordered on coauthorship. Illustrations were drawn by Raymond Molina and Robert L. Price, and the typing of various manuscript drafts was done by Florence J. Kottlowski, Karen S. Kottlowski, and Sharon L. Ballenger. Appreciation and credit, as indicated in the text, is given those individuals and organizations that have permitted the reproduction of drawings and photographs.

PREFACE

The writer has attempted to cover every common facet of section measuring in this manual, to be of use not only to geologists, but to others who work with layered rocks and sediments, such as soil scientists, engineers, hydrologists, archeologists, and geophysicists. Suggestions, additions, and constructive criticism from readers and users are welcome.

Socorro, New Mexico F. E. K.
February, 1965

Contents

Editor's Foreword v
Preface vii

1 PURPOSES OF MEASURING SECTIONS 1
Stratigraphic studies 2
Subsurface correlation 6
Geologic mapping 11
Type sections 16
Paleontologic control 18
Sedimentation studies 19
Control for deciphering structure 24
Control for compositional trends 26
Control for sampling 28

2 SELECTING A SECTION FOR STUDY 31
Types of exposures 36
Topography 40
Structure 43
Accessibility 44
Limitations 45
Route of measurements 47
Choice of units 49
General field procedure 52

CONTENTS

3 TECHNIQUES FOR ESTABLISHING CONTROL 59
  Direct contact measurements 60
  Jacob-staff measurements 61
  Eye-height measurements 75
  Plane-table and telescopic alidade techniques 92
  Transit and tape measurements 109
  Brunton compass and tape measurements 112
  Brunton compass and pace measurements 119
  Measurements from maps and photographs 122
  Altimeter measurements 125
  Rapid estimates by pace and dip 129
  Combinations of control techniques 130

4 TYPES OF MEASUREMENTS 139
  Horizontal layers 139
  Vertical layers 140
  Inclined layers 146
  Measurements parallel to the strike 165

5 ERRORS IN MEASUREMENTS 168
  Precision and accuracy 170
  Mechanical errors 172
  Boundaries of measured units 173
  Covered intervals 173
  Correlation across faults 175
  Offsets in section traverses 177

CONTENTS

6 DESCRIPTION OF MEASURED UNITS 180
Sedimentary rocks 182
Layered igneous rocks 209
Metamorphic rocks 214
Graphic presentation 215
Final presentation 219

APPENDIX 225

Table 1. Correction of eye-height measurements for dip 227

Table 2. Stratigraphic thickness from dip and horizontal distance measured normal to strike 229

Table 3. Natural sines, cosines, tangents, and cotangents 230

Table 4. Abbreviations for descriptions of measured units 232

Table 5. Simple trigonometric relations 236

REFERENCES CITED 239

INDEX 247

Measuring
Stratigraphic
Sections

1 □ Purposes of Measuring Sections

What is a measured stratigraphic section? Measuring a stratigraphic section consists of: (1) determining the thickness, and (2) describing each layered unit in a rock sequence, as well as (3) noting the relationships to adjoining rock units. The term "measure" thus is used in a broad sense, meaning more than determination of dimension, covering the entire field process. The individual measurements and descriptions are combined into a tabular descriptive report on the rocks; this is the measured stratigraphic section. The object is to measure the thickness of a wide slice of the earth's crust and to describe the lithology, fossils, thickness, and interrelationships of individual units within a stratigraphic sequence.

Measured sections constitute the main working tool for stratigraphic studies, a necessity for the interpretation of subsurface sequences, and the basis for defining geologic units dealt with in areal mapping. Collections of fossils, rock specimens, and other materials for lithologic, economic, and paleontologic studies should be labeled as to their precise location in measured sections. In areas of complex geologic structure, measured sections of the complete layered sequence commonly are necessary to determine local or regional relations.

Measurements must be made by methods that permit reasonably quick and accurate work. Lateral variations in the measured units should be noted, so that the section can be related to an area rather than just to the gully, slope, or ridge where the actual details are determined. Sedimentary beds and many other types of geologic units are fundamentally lenticular, which imposes practical limits on the desirable precision and detail necessary from a single section. There is little point in using a microtome to cut butter!

STRATIGRAPHIC STUDIES

Stratigraphy, the study and interpretation of stratified rocks, is concerned with the identification, description, vertical and horizontal relations, mapping, and correlation of layered rock units. Weller (1960) listed the successive steps for over-all stratigraphic studies as: (1) discrimination of stratigraphic units, (2) determination of the stratigraphic sequence, (3) geologic mapping, (4) stratigraphic correlation by both physical and paleontologic means, and (5) stratigraphic interpretation. Thus the bases of any such studies, the discrimination of units and the determination of the sequence, are keyed into measurements of stratigraphic sections.

In their broadest sense, stratigraphic studies almost completely cover the fields of geology dealing with rocks and other natural materials that are layered. All these studies are based upon measured sections of particular sequences. Even a quick glance through the various geologic journals, publications of federal and state geological surveys, and books on every geologic subject shows that more than half are directly concerned with stratigraphy or depend on stratigraphic studies for supporting data. In general geologic reports, representing the primary studies for many areas, the earliest chapters in most cases are descriptions of the stratigraphic sequence and include one or more measured sections.

Typical examples of reports dealing principally with stratigraphy, deciphered on the basis of numerous measured sections, are:

1. *Cambrian Formations and Sections in Part of Cordilleran Trough* (Deiss, 1938), which describes the strata and fossils for a particular system of rocks
2. *Late Paleozoic Stratigraphy of Central Cochise County, Arizona* (Gilluly, Cooper, and Williams, 1954), which presents sections, descriptions, and faunal lists for several systems of beds throughout a region
3. *Salem Limestone and Associated Formations in South-Central Indiana* (Perry, Smith, and Wayne, 1954), which details observations for a single formation and adjacent beds
4. *Stratigraphic Studies of the San Andres Mountains, New Mexico* (Kottlowski, Flower, Thompson, and Foster, 1956), which presents stratigraphic data for the rock units exposed within a mountain range

PURPOSES OF MEASURING SECTIONS

Whereas the sections in these reports may have been measured foot by foot, they commonly are summarized by columnar sections, like that in Fig. 1–1, which show the gross lithology on scales ranging from 5 feet to an inch to 500 feet to an inch.

When the geologist looks at the rocks and observes their physical characteristics, such as thickness, bedding,

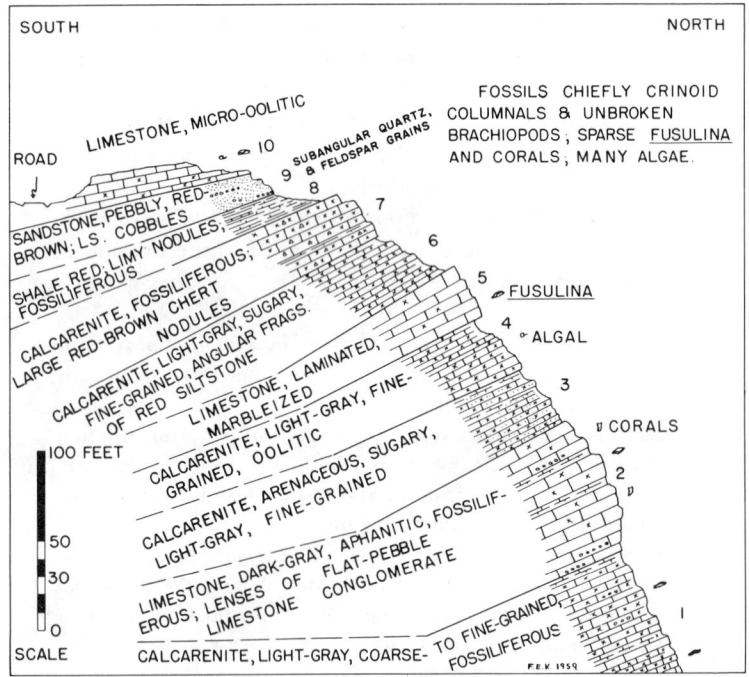

Fig. 1–1. Trout Creek columnar section, west-central New Mexico.

mineral composition, color, and contained fossils, the purpose of stratigraphic studies—interpretation of the geologic history—should be kept in mind. Gathering of the physical data is only a start toward this goal. The raw description of a stratigraphic sequence usually leads to preparation of useful correlation tables, cross sections, columnar sections, geologic maps, isopach maps, and lithofacies maps; but these in turn are only devices to aid in fuller interpretation of the fundamental data, to deduce the geologic history, paleogeography, and sedimental patterns.

The measuring of stratigraphic sections generally is applied to sequences of sediments and sedimentary rocks, including the volcanic sediments such as tuffs. However, extrusive igneous rocks are commonly layered, even if only in an over-all tabular manner, and also are susceptible to stratigraphic studies and measurements, as are some layered intrusive igneous bodies and most sequences of metamorphic rocks. Such operations all too often are omitted on the grounds that the thickness and lithology of volcanic rocks are too variable to be of use, or the units are too thick and too uniform in composition for a measured section to be of significance. Neither of these arguments is valid for many occurrences.

Gilbert (1938), in his classic study of the Bishop welded tuff, referred to "sections" and divided the tuff into members based on local measurements of thickness and differences in detailed lithology. Thus even a relatively uniform extrusive rock may be studied stratigraphically. Larsen and Cross (1956), in their summary of the varied igneous rocks in the San Juan Mountains of southwestern Colorado, include numerous measured stratigraphic sections of the volcanic rocks. Many of these sections are generalized to the nearest hundred feet, but they do describe the variation and similarity of volcanic lithologies and thicknesses from place to place. Such columnar-section descriptions can be very useful and provide a three-dimensional illustration that is immediately clear and describes the rocks at a known geographic location.

Stratigraphic studies, whether of sedimentary, metamorphic, or of layered igneous rocks, should begin with a sequential description of the units being investigated. As field examinations of the rocks are a fundamental element of most geologic work, the measurement and description of such stratigraphic sections are necessary in most geologic and related earth science investigations.

SUBSURFACE CORRELATION

More surface sections of sedimentary rocks are measured by petroleum geologists than by any other group in the profession. These many sections are measured not only for basic stratigraphic studies, but also for correlation with subsurface data. Other sections, though initially measured to determine surface relationships, eventually are directed toward correlation with strata penetrated by drilling. Ground-water geologists also have long recognized the advantages of measuring and closely examining known aquifers on the surface, whether these be porous sandstones such as the Dakota Sandstone, cavernous limestones like the San Andres Limestone, or beds of loosely consolidated sand and gravel. Possible subsurface characteristics can be observed

SUBSURFACE CORRELATION

from surface outcrops whether the beds may be uniform for hundreds of miles as with the Dakota and San Andres formations, or may be extremely lenticular like many sand and gravel beds.

Petroleum geology and ground-water hydrology in particular, and mining geology and engineering geology in part, are in a somewhat separate category from other geologic studies. They are dependent upon a thorough basic knowledge of stratigraphy, but this involves not only surface outcrops but also the correlation and translation from these surface rocks to the subsurface sections penetrated by the drill. The chief problem, once surface beds have been measured and wells drilled, is one of correlating between rocks in the outcrop and the more restricted samples, either cuttings or cores, brought up by the drilling. Some lithic features may look different, and some may *be* different.

Shaly rocks that weather to flakes and thin slabs on the surface may be massive and hard in cores. The gypsum in surface outcrops of an evaporite deposit may not be present in the correlative subsurface sequence, where anhydrite, halite, and soluble potash minerals may appear instead. The color of weathered rock surfaces, and occasionally even the color of freshly broken samples from the outcrop, may be strikingly different from that of drill-bit cuttings representing the same beds.

Determination of thickness, a primary concern in section measuring, can be a difficult problem in interpreting subsurface records, whether from a relatively shallow well drilled for water or a test hole drilled thousands of feet to "basement" rocks. The attitude of beds encountered in a hole may not be constant; moreover,

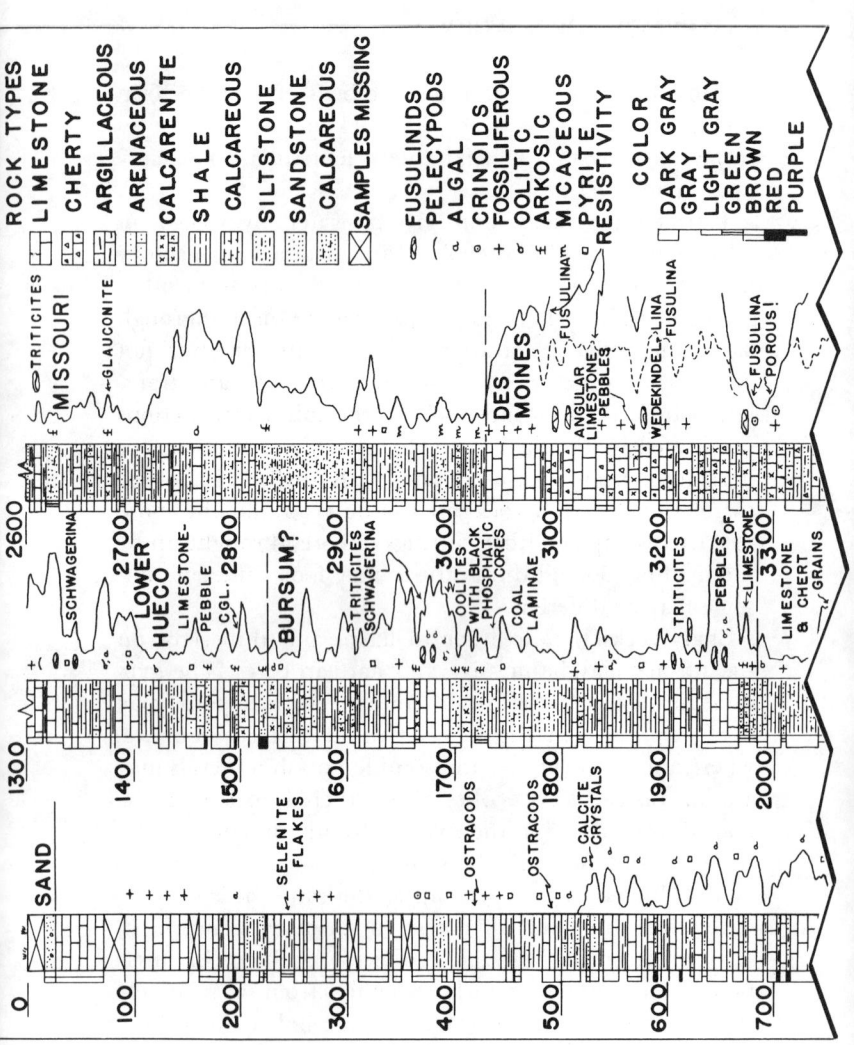

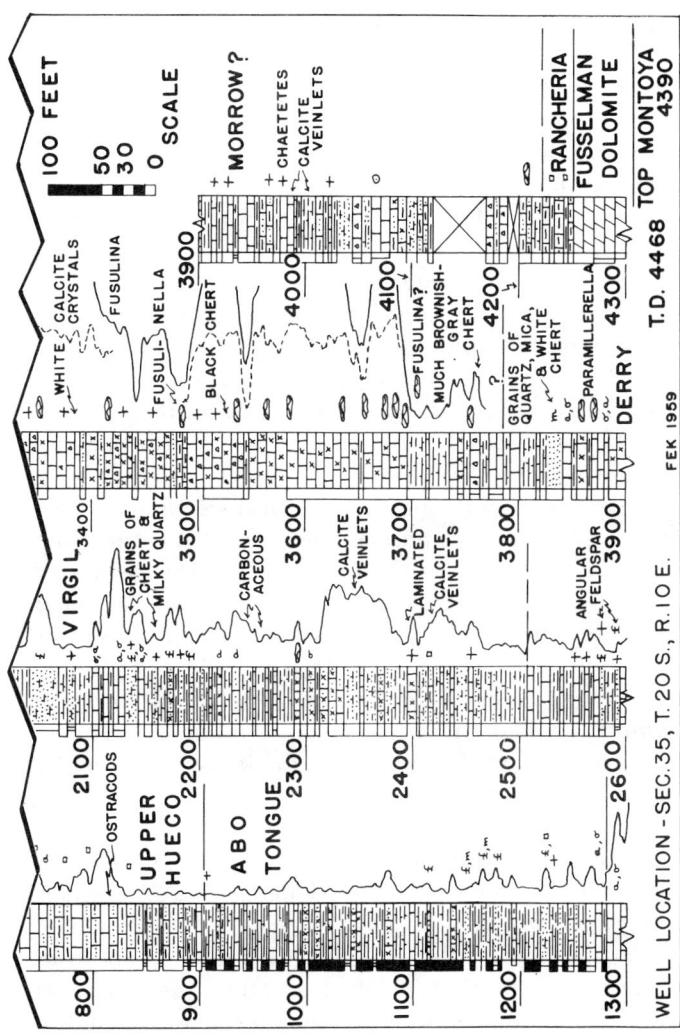

Fig. 1-2. Connected columnar section of Permian and Pennsylvanian rocks drilled in Sun No. 1 Pearson oil test.

the course of the hole itself may vary. Faults may eliminate or may duplicate parts of the sequence. Many of these breaks are difficult to recognize during drilling. Loss of strata also may result from penetration of an ancient surface of erosion, and the unconformity may be difficult to perceive or to locate on the basis of drilling data alone. These problems may be solved if a surface section is measured near the drill hole to be used for comparisons of thicknesses and other features.

Drill-hole records of beds commonly are more complete than surface measurements. The surface exposures may be interrupted by covered intervals, whereas samples ordinarily are recovered throughout most of a drill hole. To identify the lithology of drill cuttings, they must be examined under a binocular microscope; thus in many cases the cuttings are studied in more detail than those of outcrops. This is illustrated by Fig. 1-2, a connected columnar section of the rocks penetrated in an oil test drilled in south-central New Mexico. To be comparable, measuring a surface section for correlations with the subsurface should include detailed sampling of each unit and later study of the samples in the office using the binocular microscope.

The ultimate coordination of measured outcrop sections and subsurface sequences lies in the preparation, from the lithologic and faunal data, of cross sections along comparatively straight lines. Fig. 1-3, for example, shows the lateral relations of Pennsylvanian strata from western to central New Mexico. The cross section is based upon studies of seven outcrop sections and five test holes distributed along a 175-mile line. To bring out the general paleogeologic features, rather than specific details, the various beds have been combined into major lithic units.

From west to east, the cross section illustrates diagrammatically the lateral changes from the Pennsylvanian-age Zuni upland (well No. 97), which was a source of Pennsylvanian clastic sediments, eastward into the Lucero marine basin (sects. Nos. 35 and 37), thence onto the Joyita Hills-Manzanita marine shelf (sects. Nos. 47, 48, and 45; and well No. 44), thence into the Estancia depositional trough (well No. 41), and finally up onto the Pennsylvanian-age Pedernal landmass, another source of detritus during Pennsylvanian time. Correlating among the surface sections and oil tests, one can see the high percentage of clastic rocks near the source uplands, the dominance of marine limestones and shales in the basins, and the thickening and thinning of the entire Pennsylvanian sequence as well as of particular series. Shown in addition are the various rocks that underlie the erosion surface at the base of the Pennsylvanian section, as well as the several rock units that rest upon the Pennsylvanian beds. Near the Zuni upland to the west, the Abo red beds appear to grade downward into the upper Pennsylvanian rocks, whereas to the east the Abo and/or Bursum Formations are at least locally unconformable on strata of Virgilian age. In the Joyita Hills, Bursum conglomerates and sandstones rest upon an erosion surface cut down onto beds of Missourian age.

GEOLOGIC MAPPING

One of the first problems in any geologic mapping project is to determine which rock units should be

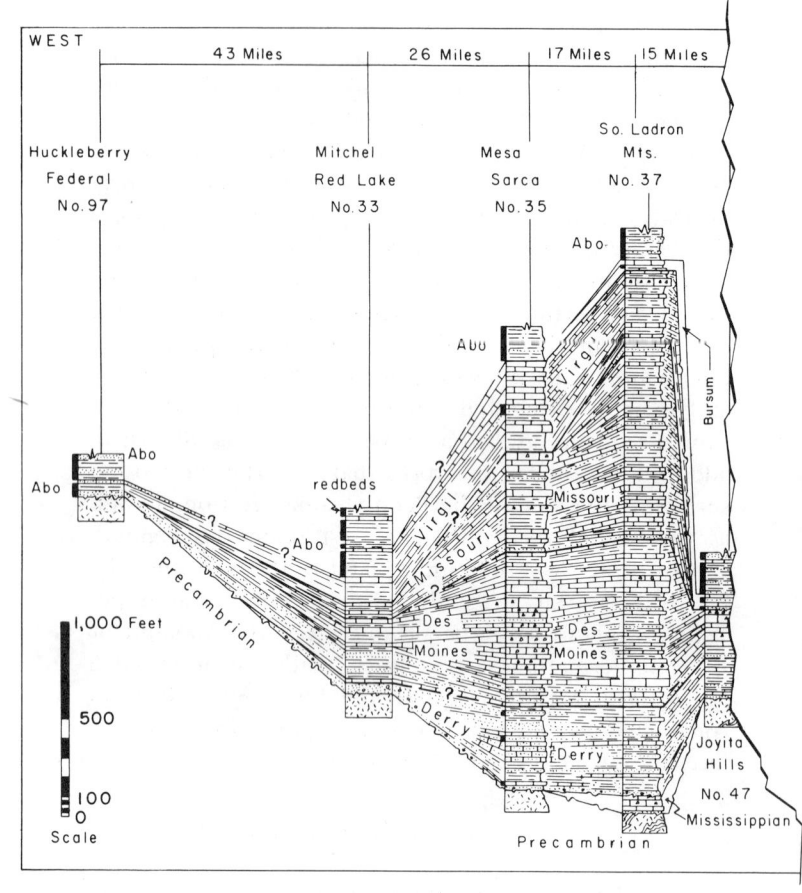

Fig. 1–3. Diagrammatic cross section of Pennsylvanian rocks

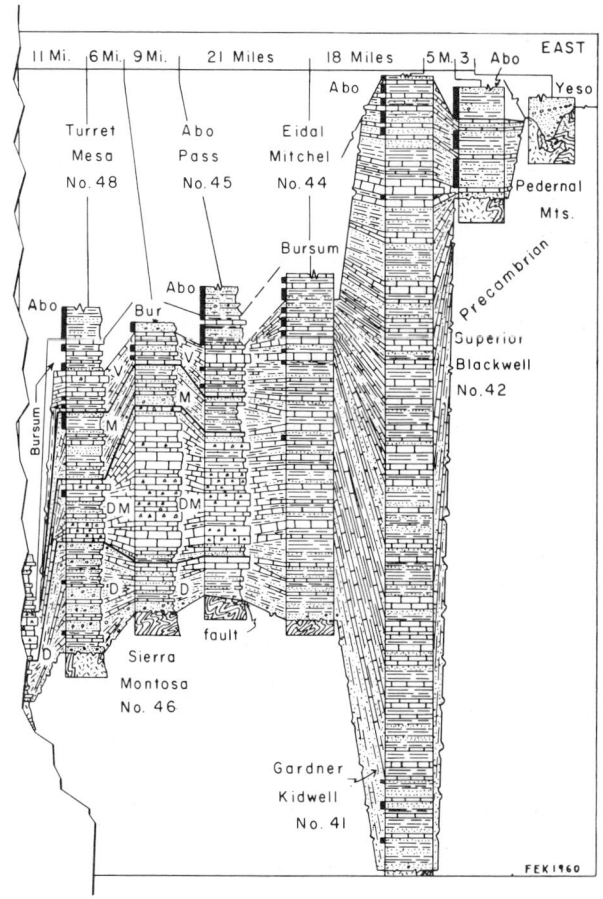

from Zuni Arch eastward to Pedernal Mountains in New Mexico.

delineated. In some essentially unexplored areas the geologist may have no more than a vague idea as to the types and ages of rocks that will be encountered. Thus he will need to make preliminary reconnaissance studies to determine his mapping units. In most parts of the United States, many of the rock units will have been defined and mapped in adjoining areas, or some units may have been recognized in the study area through earlier mapping by less detailed methods.

Depending somewhat on the time available and the amount of detail necessary, four choices are available. The geologist may begin his mapping at some likely spot, decide upon map units as he goes, and during a late stage of the project—when the distribution of stratigraphic units is known throughout the area—measure stratigraphic sections to obtain adequate descriptions of the mapped units. This procedure is desirable only when the geology is reasonably well known from previous, less detailed studies.

Another approach is to make reconnaissance traverses of the area, observing the possible map units, structure, and land forms, and then to measure stratigraphic sections at favorable localities where thick, complete sequences are well exposed. A third approach, generally most desirable in an area of low relief and gently dipping beds, is to do the geologic mapping and the measuring of stratigraphic sections more or less simultaneously. Such sections usually are thin, and they should be closely spaced.

The fourth possibility, applicable particularly for areas of complex geology, is to begin with some mapping, then

GEOLOGIC MAPPING

measure some sections, followed by more mapping, and then some more measuring of stratigraphic sections. This procedure is often necessary where a geologist must map to learn the location of measurable sections and then must measure some sections to aid in mapping.

Unless geologic mapping is done only in generalized reconnaissance, measured stratigraphic sections are necessary to record in a logical manner the lithology and thicknesses of the beds and other units, as well as the over-all characteristics of the formations. If any considerable lateral extent of a formation is exposed, several sections should be measured in order to recognize and illustrate lateral variations or lateral similarities in lithology and thickness. The detailed data obtained from measuring and describing several sections should be supplemented by careful observation of the lateral changes within mapped units between the section localities. Such a combination of section measuring, detailed geologic observation, and mapping provides facts with which to decipher the geologic history of the area, as well as the three-dimension relationships of the lithologic sections. This knowledge can lead to recognition of features that otherwise would go unnoticed, and in some instances results in discovery of economically valuable deposits.

Aerial photographs are widely used in geologic mapping, both in the field and in the office. Examination of features revealed on such photographs, if backed by a knowledge of the rock units that might be present, may permit the geologist to do much of his "mapping" in the office. Such photogeologic mapping, however, should be checked in the field, especially by the measuring of sections in many localities. (See Lattman and Ray, *Aerial Photographs in Field Geology*, in this series.)

TYPE SECTIONS

The American Commission on Stratigraphic Nomenclature set up a revised code in 1961, mainly to provide a usefully comprehensive, yet explicit statement of principles and practices for classifying and naming stratigraphic units, and to promote the greatest possible uniformity in applying these principles and practices. This code, which deals chiefly with layered rocks and rock units but is applicable to all kinds of rocks—sedimentary, igneous, and metamorphic—has been widely accepted by American geologists and geologic organizations.

To formally establish a rock-stratigraphic unit, a type area should be indicated and a type section measured, described, and accurately located. Thus one of the chief prerequisites for properly naming and identifying a stratigraphic unit is the measurement and description of a type section. If possible, this section should lie within or near the geographic feature from which the name of the unit is derived. For example, the type section of the Hueco Formation is in the Hueco Mountains of western Texas, and that of the St. Louis Limestone is near the city of St. Louis in Missouri.

Specific reference to the location of each type section according to section, township, range, or other land divisions should be given; a map showing the precise location of the measured section also is necessary. De-

TYPE SECTIONS

scription of the unit should include: (1) distinguishing characteristics, (2) definition of contact relations, (3) dimensions and shape, and (4) geologic age and correlation, if known. For the type section, lithologic descriptions of the individual beds and measured units, their measured thicknesses, topographic expression, lateral variation, and fossil content should be noted. All of these items should be published in some recognized scientific medium, such as any well-known, regularly issued, numbered series.

Fig. 1–4 is an example of a geologic reference map

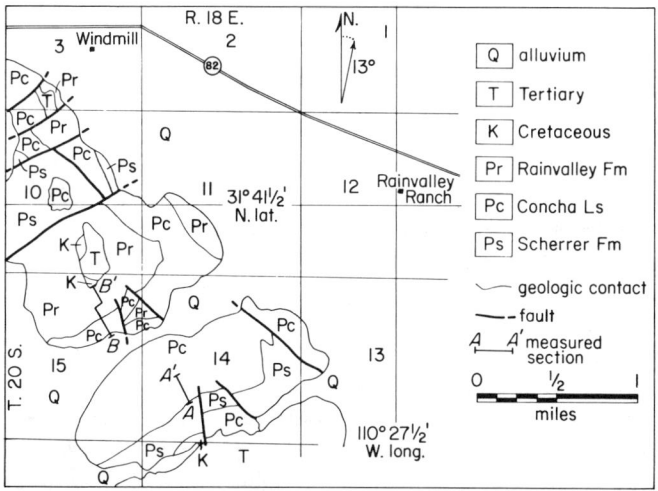

Fig. 1–4. Geologic reference map of northern Mustang Mountains showing location of type section of Rainvalley Formation (modified from Bryant and McClymonds, 1961; geologic mapping by D. L. Bryant).

showing the location of the type section of the Rainvalley Formation, a Permian unit defined and studied by Bryant and McClymonds (1961) in southeastern Arizona. Location of the measured section, the type section, is indicated by the heavy line *B-B'*. In addition, the authors describe this type section, and note the distribution, variance in thickness, and over-all characteristics of the formation as well as describing its contained fauna. They also provide a series of columnar sections showing the correlation of the type section with measured sections of the Rainvalley Formation in other areas. Complete assemblages of such data should document the naming of any newly established stratigraphic unit.

PALEONTOLOGIC CONTROL

To be of maximum value in stratigraphic correlation and paleontologic studies, every fossil, every fauna, and every flora should be located as to position in the stratigraphic sequence. If fossils are collected at a distance from a measured section, their horizons of occurrence should be traced out to this section or their proper stratigraphic positions otherwise established. Vertical changes in faunas, the appearance or disappearance of index fossils, and imperceptible vertical gradations between different faunas and floras may take place within an apparently uniform lithic unit. Thus it is necessary to record not only the stratigraphic location of a unit containing a specific fossil, but also the horizon of the fossil within the unit, especially if the unit is thick.

The selection of lithologic units in section measuring, as well as their identification and formal or informal designation, are arbitrary procedures dictated mainly by the practical requirements of the particular geologic study. There is no assurance that each of these units will prove to contain a single fauna or flora throughout; indeed, the contained faunas generally vary throughout any thick unit, either in response to evolutionary control or in adaption to ecologic control. Faunal and floral zones may not be well defined, measurable units in the outcrop. Therefore, the fossil zones must be precisely located in the measured section to be useful as paleontologic control.

Collections of microfossils in particular should be correlated with a measured section. Precise location of the fossiliferous beds is likely to be critical because the faunas and floras of microfossils may change rapidly in a short vertical interval.

An example of the location of fossil collections within measured sections is shown in Fig. 1–5, which includes two measured columnar sections of Mississippian beds in northern New Mexico. Reasonably exact locations of the fossiliferous zones were especially desirable in this instance since these Mississippian strata had previously been classified as partly of either Pennsylvanian or Devonian age.

SEDIMENTATION STUDIES

Sedimentation studies can be grouped into two general categories: (1) detailed investigations of the sediments or parts thereof, such as the heavy minerals of sandstones within a certain sequence, or the clay fraction of all rocks within a series of strata, and (2) broader

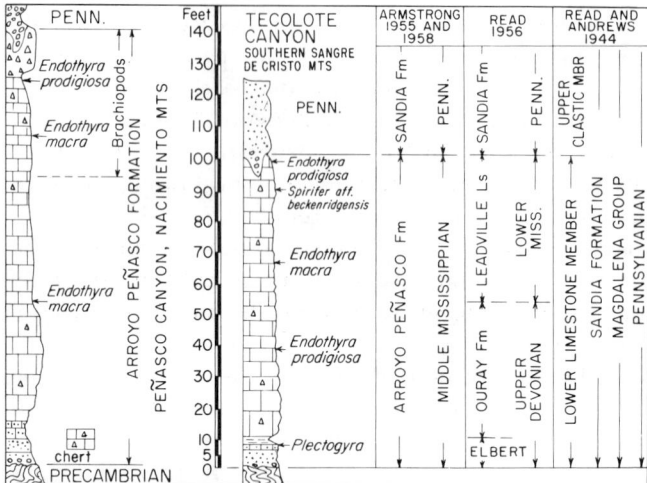

Fig. 1–5. Spacing of fossil collections within measured sections of Arroyo Peñasco Formation in northern New Mexico (modified from Armstrong, 1958).

studies of all deposits of a certain age laid down over a wide area. Both of these types of work require the measurement of many stratigraphic sections. The first type necessitates close, careful examination, description, and sampling of the sequences in the field, followed by detailed and often painstaking laboratory work. For the second type of study, more general features are emphasized. During section measuring, the beds are treated as comparatively thick stratigraphic units in order to correlate groups of beds and sequences of groups over long distances, thereby deducing the three-dimensional relations of depositional basins, various facies, overlap of some sequences, and other elements of similar regional sedimentation.

The data obtained in regional studies can be presented in series of diagrammatic cross sections (Fig. 1-3), as fence diagrams, or plotted on isopach maps, lithofacies maps (such as that in Fig. 1-6), paleogeographic maps, or other maps that feature particular sedimentational characteristics. Fig. 1-6 illustrates the extent of gypsum, total thickness of shales, and the areal distribution of arkosic and feldspathic sandstones in the Pennsylvanian strata of south-central New Mexico. The basic data were obtained by measuring numerous stratigraphic sections and examining the cuttings from the oil tests in the region. The location of thick shale sections and the areal extent of the feldspar-rich sandstones indicate derivation of clastic materials from the Pedernal landmass; the gypsum was deposited in a late-stage evaporite basin between the Pedernal landmass and the Florida islands.

Measuring and sampling of sections for detailed studies of sediments, such as the heavy-mineral fraction of sandstones, is somewhat similar to that for microfossils. The location of the samples within a measured section should be recorded accurately.

Three stratigraphic sections measured as control for sedimentary studies are shown in Fig. 1-7. These sections are of Upper Cretaceous beds in the Todilto Park area of New Mexico, a sequence of intertongued sandstones, shales, and some coals. Willard (1963) zoned these beds on the bases of heavy-mineral suites, percentage of feldspars, soluble fractions, and angularity of the grains. The boundaries of the heavy-mineral zones in some

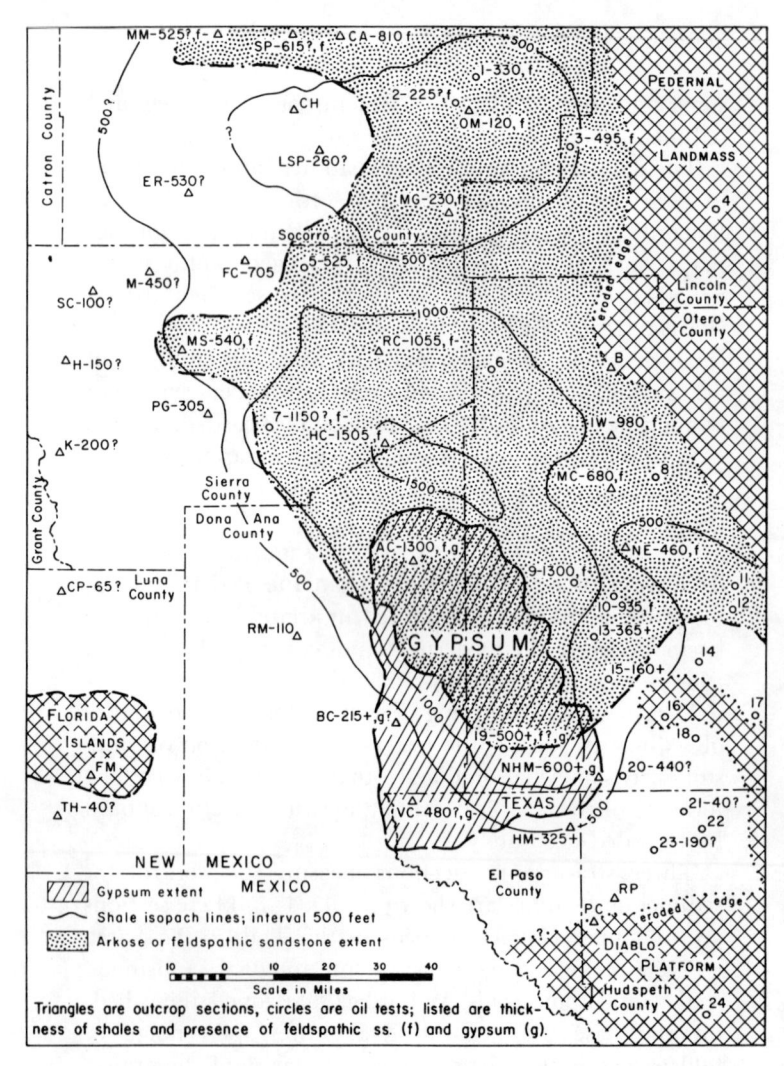

Fig. 1–6. "GSA" map for Pennsylvanian of south-central New Mexico. Gypsum extent, shale isopach, and arkosic sandstone extent.

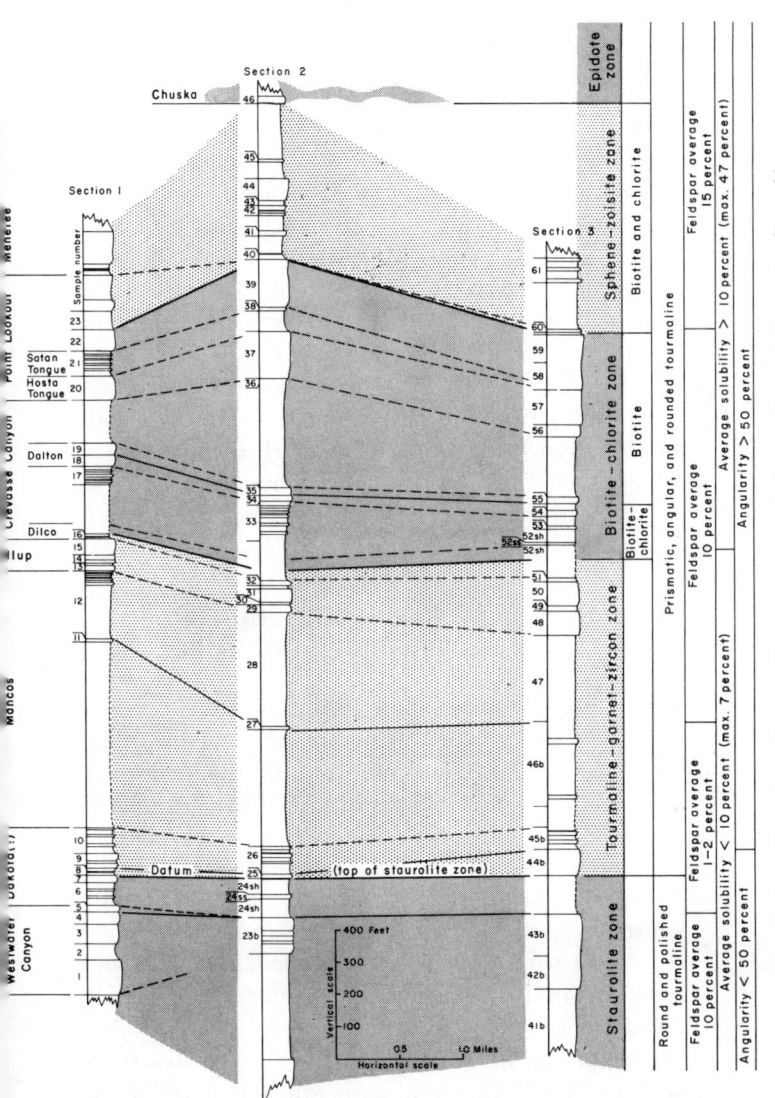

Fig. 1-7. Stratigraphic sections measured for sedimentology studies. Upper Cretaceous rocks in Todilto Park, New Mexico (Willard, 1963).

places do not parallel formation boundaries, emphasizing the need for detailed control of the sampling by precisely measured sections. Much of the value of detailed, painstaking field and laboratory work can be lost if the samples are not accurately correlated with carefully measured sections.

Studies of varved clays and of soils are specialized work in sedimentation. As most varves are less than an inch thick, this type of section measuring deals with very thin units, and very many units. Soil profiles, which are measured sections of the various horizons of a soil, in contrast, generally consist of only three main units, the *A*, *B*, and *C* soil horizons with minor subdivisions, and are measured in inches and feet rather than in fractions of an inch.

CONTROL FOR DECIPHERING STRUCTURE

Measured stratigraphic sections are highly desirable in studies of geologic structure, whether they deal with mapping of folds, faults, unconformities, and other features, or with the preparation of structure cross sections or contour maps. To decipher complicated geologic structures, it is vital to a geologist to know where specific beds occur in the normal stratigraphic sequence, to know how thick are the various rock units, and to know what (and where) sedimentational discontinuities are in the sequence. This information is best obtained from measured sections.

The emphasis in measuring sections for structural work is on the thickness of units and areal variations

CONTROL FOR DECIPHERING STRUCTURE

in thickness, gross lithology or distinctive characteristics of the lithology, and positions of key beds, marker beds, or other units. If possible, the sections should be in areas where the geologic structure is simple.

Stratigraphic units may be structurally thickened or thinned in some areas. Shale beds, for example, may be thickened along crests of anticlines and troughs of synclines, and thinned along the limbs of these folds. Massive competent beds, such as thick limestones, when subject to compressive stresses leading to development of numerous imbricate thrust slices, may form thick successions of repeated beds. Some of the possible chaotic relations due to imbricate thrust faulting are shown on Fig. 1–8, a generalized cross section of part of the Sawtooth Mountains of Montana (Deiss, 1943). In such areas of intimately faulted strata, true thicknesses may be difficult to determine, because even major thrust faults may not be readily apparent on the outcrop. Measured sections in the Sawtooth Mountains and in adjoining

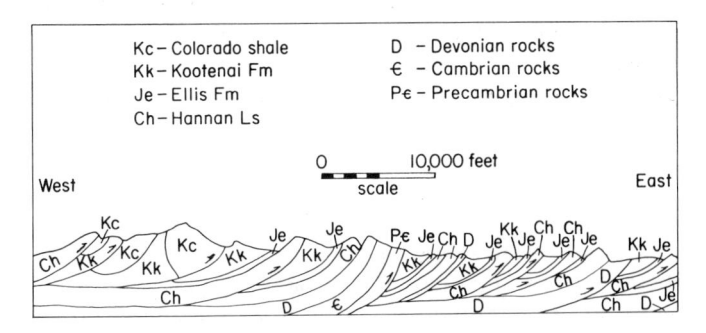

Fig. 1–8. Imbricate thrust faulting in Sawtooth Mountains of Montana (modified from Deiss, 1943).

areas where the structure is less complex were of essential aid in deciphering the chaotic structure.

CONTROL FOR COMPOSITIONAL TRENDS

Lithology, perhaps even minute variances in lithology, is the chief clue to compositional trends whether due to original deposition or to diagenetic changes. Closely spaced measured sections, with emphasis on lithologic or mineralogical details, are necessary to distinguish these local and regional facies trends. Examples of compositional trends within sedimentary rocks are (1) changes in the composition of coal beds within coal basins, (2) variations in carbonate-rock units from limestone to dolomite, (3) gradations of marine limestone or marine shale shoreward into shoreline sediments, and hence into terrestrial beds, and (4) intertonguing of marine shelf sediments with reef deposits and then laterally into lagoonal and shoreline rocks. Layered intrusive rocks commonly show compositional changes either of specific minerals or changes in rock types. Metamorphic rock layers may have systematic changes in rock types or in metamorphic "index" minerals with progressive increase in the metamorphic rank; measured sections are useful in documenting these distribution variations.

One of the pronounced changes in rock composition, both laterally and vertically, is that in evaporite deposits. Ideally, there should be lateral gradation inward from the edge of the saline basin, a change from red beds into limestones and dolomites, thence progressively into anhydrite with limestone laminae, anhydrite, halite, and finally, in rare cases, into bittern salts such as potash minerals in the center of the basin. Most evaporite deposits actually are much more complex in their three-dimensional distribution; parts of the sequences may be removed by erosion or altered by solution and recrystallization; but stratigraphic sections measured along diameters of the saline basin may reveal the compositional changes and provide data for predictions as to where beds of commercial salines occur.

Measured stratigraphic sections of volcanic rocks, spaced as closely as necessary, can usefully show changes in composition and thickness of rock types, and can aid considerably in the correlation of some layered units. If, for example, a thick and extensive sequence of layered volcanic rocks, such as flows, tuffs, welded tuffs, breccias, and volcanic sandstones, were derived from two large shield volcanoes, and if they appeared as intertonguing rock lenses originating from these two centers, changes in lithology and thickness as measured in stratigraphic sections should indicate the general location of the eruptive centers, and allow deductions as to the sequence of the eruptions.

Capps' (1915) study of the White River ash fall in southeastern Alaska and southwestern Yukon Territory illustrates the use of measured thicknesses to deduce the source of a large volcanic eruption. He gathered data on measured sections of this 1400-year-old ash, and plotted and contoured the thicknesses. This showed that (1) the eruption occurred on the north flank of the St. Elias Mountains, (2) the winds at the time of the eruption were from the west and south, (3) the ash is a foot or more feet thick in the windward direction for a least 220 miles from the center, and (4) more than 10 cubic miles of ash were ejected. Changes from the center outward are not only in thicknesses, but also in decreasing grain size and minor changes in composition of the grains.

CONTROL FOR SAMPLING

The use of measured stratigraphic sections for sampling control already has been noted in connection with subsurface correlation, the collection of megafossils and microfossils, and the collections of materials for sediment studies. Even for normal stratigraphic studies, in which the emphasis is on thickness and general lithology, a hand specimen of each distinctive rock type should be collected for future reference.

Rock samples obtained for specific purposes should be located as to their precise stratigraphic position within a measured section. Such sampling includes that of (1) commercially useful rocks like high-calcium limestones, kaolin, bentonite, coal, chromite-bearing serpentine, and many others, (2) rocks collected to be chemically analyzed for traces of hydrocarbons, organic material, geochemical trace-element control, and the like, (3) rock slices for petrographic studies, (4) oriented samples to be used in petrographic orientation or microstructural studies, and (5) rocks containing enough radioactive elements to be usable for dating by analyses of radioactive decay.

Effective sampling of layered industrial rocks depends heavily upon the control provided by an accurately measured stratigraphic section. For example, Fig. 1-9 shows the Mississippian limestone units sampled from the

CONTROL FOR SAMPLING

Radcliff and Berry quarry in southern Indiana, as well as the percentage of calcium carbonate from the various units (Patton, 1949; Perry, Smith, and Wayne, 1954).

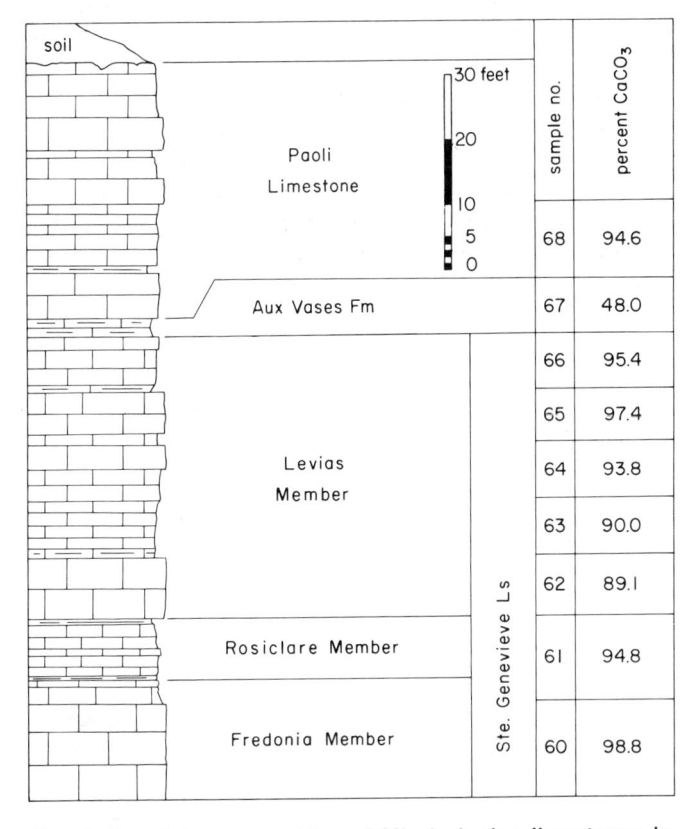

Unit		sample no.	percent CaCO$_3$
Paoli Limestone			
		68	94.6
Aux Vases Fm		67	48.0
Levias Member	Ste. Genevieve Ls	66	95.4
		65	97.4
		64	93.8
		63	90.0
		62	89.1
Rosiclare Member		61	94.8
Fredonia Member		60	98.8

Fig. 1–9. Columnar section of Mississippian limestones in Radcliff and Berry Quarry, south-central Indiana, showing chemical analyses of units.

Samples 62 to 64 and 67 contain too much magnesium carbonate and samples 61 and 68 too much silica to be used as high-calcium limestone. If an analysis had been made of a sample representing the entire section, the presence of high-calcium limestones (samples 60, 65, and 66) could have gone unnoticed. Guided by the chemical analyses of units in the measured section, a four-step quarrying operation could be carried out: (1) quarry the Paoli Limestone for crushed stone and discard the Aux Vases shaly beds, (2) quarry units 65 and 66 for lime, (3) quarry units 61 through 64 for crushed stone, and (4) quarry unit 60 as high-calcium limestone to make lime.

2 □ Selecting a Section for Study

The most desirable place to measure a stratigraphic section is where the entire sequence of interest is completely exposed in a small area and is not broken by faults or seriously modified by other structural complications. As this set of favorable conditions is rarely found, the geologist must seek the best existing combination of rock exposures, topography, and geologic structure that satisfies the requirements of accessibility and available time, funds, equipment, and personnel.

Two hours spent in the office locating possible sections on maps and photographs may save two days of work in the field. If the investigator is so fortunate as to have at his disposal geologic maps, topographic maps, and stereoscopic-paired aerial photographs for the area of study, he should be able to select the most favorable sites for section measuring in short order. Even a reconnaissance geologic map is useful in showing the approximate outcrop areas of designated formations, and in revealing major elements of geologic structure. On a detailed geologic map, the actual location for measuring a section may be found quickly. Topographic maps can be helpful in fixing the location of steep slopes, narrow canyons, cut banks of streams, and other places where rocks are likely to be well exposed. Stereoscopic pairs of vertical aerial photographs permit indirect viewing of the outcrops, and the investigator thereby can make preliminary judgments as to the adequacy of exposures, effects of structure, and how much of the sequence is present.

Looking for a satisfactory place to measure a section really begins with looking for areas of good exposures. Much frustration and expense can be saved through careful, systematic planning. Search of the pertinent geologic literature and study of available maps and photographs should be followed by a field reconnaissance of the possible sites for measuring stratigraphic sections. However, before going into the field, other problems such as access to the field locality and available transportation should be considered (see Lahee, 1961; Compton, 1960; Low, 1957).

The geologic literature in most cases will include some references to the beds to be measured, at least in adjoining areas, and some description of the areal geology. In the United States, publications and geologic bibliographies checked should include those of state geologic surveys, the U.S. Geological Survey, the American Association of Petroleum Geologists, the Geological Society of America, and other, more specialized geologic journals

TYPES OF EXPOSURES

and bibliographies, as well as geologic publications of universities and unpublished student theses.

Concurrently with a search of the geologic literature, all pertinent maps and aerial photographs should be examined. Geologic maps are a part of the geologic literature and are available from the same organizations. To see what geologic maps are available, the investigator should obtain a geologic map index of the region from the state geological survey, from the regional office of the U.S. Geological Survey, or from the files in geologic sections of most university libraries. Topographic maps, if available, can be bought from the topographic branch of the U.S. Geological Survey or are resold by various state agencies and local map suppliers. Indexes to topographic mapping in every state of the United States can be ordered, free of charge, from the Map Information Office, U.S. Geological Survey, Washington, D.C. for states east of the Mississippi River, or from the Topographic Division, U.S. Geological Survey, Denver, Colorado, for states west of the Mississippi.

Planimetric maps, showing streams, culture, and some elements of topography, can be obtained from various state and federal agencies such as the U.S. Soil Conservation Service, U.S. Forest Service, U.S. Bureau of Land Management, and state highway and geological departments. Highway maps, either of quadrangle areas or of counties, are available from many state highway departments. Some of these maps are provided at scales as large as a mile to an inch, and show drainage, culture, cliffs, and land control grids (section, township, and range), as well as roads and trails. If no detailed maps are available, the investigator may find himself "up a creek" both figuratively and actually, since field reconnaissance up stream valleys may then become his best means for locating measurable stratigraphic sections.

Vertical aerial photographs can be obtained from such federal agencies as the Forest Service, Soil Conservation Service, Agricultural Stabilization and Conservation Service, Air Force, Coast and Geodetic Survey, and Geological Survey, as well as from many commercial companies. Initial requests for information on aerial photography should be made to the U.S. Geological Survey; this organization keeps a record of all aerial photography flown in the United States. In other countries, geological surveys also should be among the first agencies contacted regarding the availability of aerial photographs. Photograph indexes are prepared by the various organizations supplying aerial photographs; by reference to the index of the study region, the investigator can order the individual photographs that will cover the areas where it may be possible to measure a section.

These photographs, when viewed stereoscopically, show vegetation patterns, larger outcrops, drainage lines, differences in surface color correlated with various rock types, and the topography in great detail (Lattman and Ray, 1965). Possible sites for measuring sections can be identified on the aerial photographs by observing where thick sequences are well exposed within short distances in areas of relatively simple geologic structure. Lateral variations in lithology and thickness of units often can be deduced from the photographs by the extent of resistant and nonresistant beds. In many instances, the geologist can locate a line for section measuring on aerial photographs, and then go directly to the outcrops and

TYPES OF EXPOSURES

make his measurements without any searching in the field.

Reconnaissance field searching for suitable areas is necessary if favorable localities for section measuring cannot be firmly identified in the office. By applying knowledge gleaned from the literature and employing maps and photographs first studied in the office, considerable pertinent ground can be covered quickly, an over-all idea grasped as to the thickness and lithology of the units to be measured, and choices made of any desired number of section localities. First targets of the reconnaissance are the sites determined on photographs in the office; then a brief search should be made along the strike of the units to check for better exposures and for any lateral variation in the rock units to be measured and described.

If no accurate geologic maps or aerial photographs are available, reconnaissance field traverses should be concentrated in areas most likely to include good exposures, and their pattern should be consonant with a spacing of measured sections adequate for the purposes of the study. In mountainous country, major canyons and any steep, short tributary canyons are first targets. In rolling lowlands such as those of the midwestern and southern states, stream-cut banks and side gullies are likely locations of clean natural exposures. Man-made exposures, such as cuts for railroads, highways, and open-pit mining, also provide excellent localities for section measurement and study. In areas where there is little soil cover, sections can be measured across ledges on ridge sides, along noses of ridges, in gullies, and almost any place where the combination of surface slope and dip of the beds exposes a section; in contrast, where soil and vegetative cover is thick and extensive, outcrops are limited to such areas as steep slopes, deeply cut stream channels, and man-made cuts.

TYPES OF EXPOSURES

An analysis of the types of exposures favorable for measuring stratigraphic sections is an extension of interpreting geomorphic processes that produce clean surfaces on natural materials. Hence it is necessary to consider the effects of the factors (Thornbury, 1954) that influence rock weathering and help control outcrop distribution. These factors are climate, topography, lithology, rock structure, and vegetation. Outcrops will be found most commonly on (1) steep slopes cut in (2) resistant rocks exposed mainly owing to (3) mechanical weathering in a (4) dry climate where (5) little vegetation can grow and (6) soils are thin and not much weathered rock debris, such as grus, has accumulated.

Among the numerous agencies of erosion and accompanying transportation, running water is the chief agent that sweeps away enough weathered and freshly broken bedrock to be of aid in exposing large areas of strata. In the beds of swiftly flowing streams, whether permanent or intermittent, and along cut banks of most streams, exposures are likely to be of clean rock surfaces, except for the large rivers that flow mainly in channels cut into their own alluvium. Side gullies and short, steep-gradient tributaries can provide especially choice localities (Fig. 2–1). Along steep slopes where resistant rocks occur, whether limestones in dry climates or quartz-

TYPES OF EXPOSURES

Fig. 2–1. Exposures of Mississippian limestones along side gully in Sacramento Mountains, south-central New Mexico (Pray, 1961).

ites in areas of humid climate, horizontal beds commonly form series of stepping-stone ledges, whereas steeply dipping layers tend to crop out as palisades of the harder rocks and discontinuous ledges of the less resistant rock types (Fig. 2–2).

A special case is the large glaciated region of northern and northeastern United States and much of central and eastern Canada, as well as other similar glaciated regions in Europe and elsewhere. In many parts of the glaciated areas, especially near the southern margins, bedrock is buried by thick glacial drift, and the main rock exposures are in deeply cut stream valleys or project up through the drift as isolated hills or as cores of drumlins. In contrast, the northern parts of the North American glaciated region were extensively scoured by the glaciers, much of the soil and loose alluvium was removed, and large areas of bare rock were exposed even on comparatively level surfaces.

In more humid regions, where annual precipitation is greater than 30 inches, relatively thick soils and dense vegetation are common, and even along streams outcrops of bedrock tend to be spotty and discontinuous. Tenacious rocks such as quartzite, well-cemented sandstone, and slate may form bluffs on hillsides (Fig. 2–3) or other

Fig. 2–2. Palisades of Paleozoic limestones northwest of Rock Creek, south-central Montana. (Photograph by Charles F. Deiss.)

Fig. 2–3. Bluff of Mansfield Sandstone in southwestern Indiana. (Photograph by George Ringer.)

slopes, but the best exposures of entire sections are restricted in many areas to man-made excavations—railway and highway cuts, pits and quarries, strip mines (Fig. 2–4), trenches, and open wells, shafts, and tunnels of large diameter. Gullies formed in response to poorly designed cultivation patterns, overgrazing, or the cutting of timber also may reveal useful intervals of bedrock.

Bedrock outcrops are at best scattered and sparse in some settings, such as glacial till and outwash plains, stream terraces, coastal plains, alluviated valleys and basins, areas of abundant loess or other wind-blown materials, gently rolling country of geomorphic maturity where soils are thick, areas of wet-warm climate where vegetation is dense, swamps, ice-covered and tundra areas, and regions of prevailingly soft rocks such as clay shales. Measured stratigraphic sections in these regions

Fig. 2–4. Outcrops in "highwall" of Commadore coal strip mine in southwestern Indiana. (Photograph by George Ringer.)

may include more "covered" intervals than rock units, with corresponding uncertainties in the thickness of some units, in part derived from possible structural complications within the covered interval.

TOPOGRAPHY

The prevailing topographic factor related to "good" outcrops is steepness of slopes. Deeply cut, steep-walled canyons, arroyos and gullies with steep banks, stream courses with steep gradients, ridges and mesas with steep sides, mountains and plateaus with steep fronts, all these are likely to provide favorable localities for measuring sections of freshly exposed bed-

TOPOGRAPHY

rock. However, even steep slopes may be modified by the influences of climate, vegetation, and local setting. Thus many very steep hillsides in the humid Blue Ridge Mountains of western Virginia and North Carolina present no outcrops, since the bedrock is concealed beneath a thick, continuous cover of soil and lush vegetation. Search for, and choice of, measuring localities hence cannot be made effectively on the basis of any single factor.

Local topographic and directional controls can be highly significant. For example, north-facing slopes in much of the United States are more covered by soil and vegetation than south-facing slopes, as they are not dried by the sun; therefore outcrops commonly are more extensive on south-facing sides of ridges, other factors being equal. Similar contrasts occur between outcrops of east- and west-facing slopes in many areas, the exposures being more extensive on the west-facing slopes where the warm afternoon sun is a major factor, or more extensive on east-facing slopes where prevailing westerly winds bring precipitation to the west-facing slopes. The V-shaped stream valleys with steep gradients, as clearly shown by contours on a topographic map, generally reveal more bedrock than wide, flat-bottomed valleys in which more gently flowing streams meander from one valley wall to the other. Even in the latter situation, however, good outcrops may be present where the stream has cut against the valley sides.

In terms of exposed outcrops, the optimum topography for measuring of stratigraphic sections is short, steep, side gullies and side canyons of major valleys cutting through ridges, mesas, and mountains. A favorable com-

Fig. 2–5. Outcrops on Sheep Mountain showing optimum topography for section measuring.

bination of sharp gullies, ledges, and cliffs on the south-facing side of Sheep Mountain, along Sly Canyon in the northern San Andres Mountains of New Mexico, is shown in Fig. 2–5. The influence of resistant and nonresistant beds on details of topography is well illustrated on this 2000-foot canyon wall.

STRUCTURE

Sections of layered rocks are best measured in areas where the geologic structure is as simple as it is possible to find. Most errors in measuring are ascribable to structural complications, such as loss or gain of some layers across a fault, variations in direction and degree of dip, and variations in thickness of beds due to sharp folding. However, some structural effects may be desirable. For example, in regions of low relief and nearly horizontal beds, good exposures are rare except along stream-cut ravines, canyons, or valleys. Even in such places, only small thicknesses of strata can be measured in one area, unless the topographic relief is large. But geometric relationships are greatly improved, even in areas of low relief, where the beds have been tilted or gently folded. On the flanks of an anticline, for example, hogback ridges are commonly developed along the more resistant beds (Fig. 2–6), and in general a thicker stratigraphic sequence is exposed within a short horizontal distance.

When strata must be measured in areas of complex structure, considerable lateral tracing of key units is advisable in order to recognize any structural thinning and thickening, dislocation of the section by faults, and

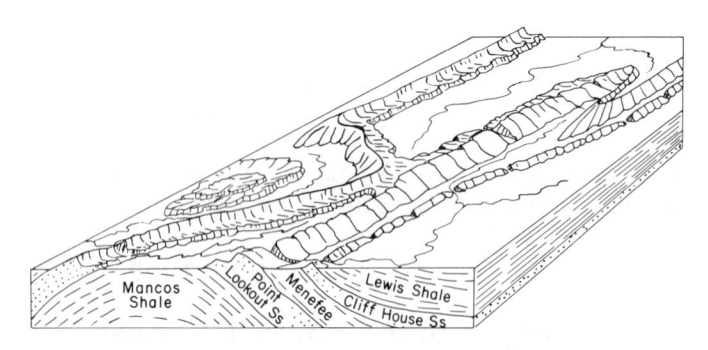

Fig. 2–6. Dipping beds on flanks of an anticline.

rapid variable changes in strikes and dips. Sedimentary structures in particular must be observed and measured sections located in consideration of depositional variations, such as lenticular beds, cross bedding on a large scale, differential erosion below unconformities, lateral changes in lithologies (from limy sandstone into arenaceous calcarenite for example), and reef complexes.

ACCESSIBILITY

Well-exposed sequences of layered rocks that are most accessible should be given prime attention. For speed in reaching the site and for convenience in handling equipment and sample materials, it is well to be a "road" geologist if possible, even if the road is merely a jeep trail. Walking should not be neglected when studying an area. A sequence of rocks, to be adequately studied and measured both vertically and laterally, must be traversed on foot. No laboratory equipment has yet been devised to replace the exploring foot, the well-guided geologic pick, the observant eye, and the active mind.

Accessibility in most areas is a question of finding where the roads and jeep trails are, either from maps and aerial photographs or through the advice of local residents. All other factors being equal, the accessibility may determine the techniques employed for section measuring. For example, it is less feasible and more costly to take a three- or four-man technical field party into a relatively remote area to measure sections by plane-table or by transit-and-tape methods than to assign a two-man team to cover the same traverse by much simpler methods.

Accessibility necessarily includes obtaining permission from the land owner or lessee to enter and work in his property or even merely to cross his property in order to reach another locality. Ranchers and farmers often have been irritated by the actions of careless persons; these range from leaving gates open, not completely dousing fires, and camping too close to watering places for ranch stock, to cutting fences and other acts of vandalism. Obtaining permission to enter a property is at least a courtesy; it also may be the only safe, sane method of operation.

LIMITATIONS

Nearly all section-measuring projects are governed by some limitations of time, funds, equipment, and personnel. These factors commonly are interrelated. The limitations of time primarily determine the techniques used, the precision and accuracy of measuring, the amount and detail of observations, the number of sections measured, and the amount of lateral tracing that is done.

Most section-measuring equipment is fairly simple and inexpensive; a short tape, folding carpenter's rule, Jacob staff, Brunton compass, hand level, Abney hand level (with clinometer), and a 100-foot tape will suffice for most techniques. In some projects a plane table, telescopic alidade, and stadia rod, or a transit, tape, and rod may be necessary; but even these more sophisticated instruments are generally available to most groups.

The number of available personnel, together with the sum of their experience, skill, personality, and ability to work effectively as a team, may affect the selection of a section or the techniques utilized to measure the rock sequence. Plane-tabling or use of the transit-and-tape method requires at least two technically trained persons, but is swifter with a party of three or four; in addition to saving time, a larger group can devote more effort to geologic observation as well as to the basic surveying procedures. Many of the simpler measuring techniques, like the Jacob staff or Hewett method described in Chapter 3, can be employed by one geologist, although a party of two may be able to do the work more thoroughly and more than twice as fast. If many samples are to be collected as part of the measuring project, as for example when working toward subsurface correlations or microfauna control, nontechnical helpers can be employed to do the collecting, packaging, and recording of samples.

A person who has difficulty in working and cooperating with others may be quite competent to measure a section alone, but he is likely to disrupt the operations of a field party to the extent that both accuracy and speed are lost. The more critical tasks should be done by the more experienced and competent member or members of the field party. In section measuring for structural control, for example, thickness measurements are critical and should be made by the best trained person available. In contrast, if a section is measured principally for paleontologic control, seeking and collecting the fossils is the most important activity and hence should be done, or closely supervised, by the most qualified member of the field party.

ROUTE OF MEASUREMENTS

Most layered rocks were formed, unit by unit, in order, from the base upward. Measuring, describing, and sampling a typical section is easier and more in rhythm with the ancient depositional trends if done in a stratigraphic sense. In part, the investigator is describing the geologic history of the sequence as he measures such a section, which thus should trace the actual sequence of geologic events. Sedimentary features, as well as many features observable in igneous and metamorphic rocks, can be best treated in stratigraphic order.

Measuring, describing, and sampling upward topographically also has distinct advantages. As most sequences have their oldest beds at the base, uphill is also upward stratigraphically. Looking upward, a person has a better view of the base and faces of rock ledges, neither of which can be seen easily from above in most situations. The upward view allows fuller observations of that part of the section that has not been seen previously and has not yet been described—the part that is "yet to come." As the sides of the beds are visible, the characteristics of the rocks over some lateral distance can be noted directly; these features include unconformities, lateral lithologic changes, and lenticularity. Places where the overlying beds are better exposed can also be recognized. Climbing or walking upward not only is more naturally correlated with observation, but it also embodies a psychological advantage in that one naturally proceeds more slowly and hence is likely to take more time and care in examining the rocks.

When sections are measured principally to provide many samples, it may be advantageous to work downward stratigraphically and topographically, like logging a drill hole. Samples are easier to carry downhill, especially as more and more are obtained while the section is being measured, and the load thus becomes heavier as the work progresses. Alternatively, a person may sample upward, leave the samples on the outcrop, and then come back down the section, picking up the samples after the section is measured.

Rarely is it possible to measure a sequence along a single, continuous traverse. To include units that are concealed by soil or slope wash in one place, measurements must be offset along traceable bedding planes to a locality of better exposure. In most areas, part of a desired sequence is well exposed in one place, whereas other parts are partly covered and must be measured at some other locality. Most measured sections, therefore, are "composite" stratigraphic sections comprising segments scattered over a considerable area. A spread-out section is not similar to the sequence penetrated in a drill hole, which represents the stratigraphic column at a single point; parts of the surface section, in contrast, may be miles from one another. In selecting a section, one should seek exposures that permit the measuring of maximum stratigraphic thickness within an area of minimum size (Fig. 2–5). As Wengerd (1955) points out, every effort should be made to locate exposures at which the beds can be measured directly instead of using slope measurements and trigonometric computations.

CHOICE OF UNITS

In the measurement of sections, any division of a layered rock sequence into various units is partly or even wholly arbitrary. For sedimentary rocks, the obvious fundamental division would be based upon the depositional unit, that is, that layer, bed, or other assemblage of sediments that were deposited under essentially constant conditions. Such units, however, commonly are impossible to recognize or to define, either at the outcrop or subsequently in the laboratory, without detailed study. For layered volcanic rocks, the simplest unit is whichever thickness of rock was extruded during a single eruption or during one of the pulses of an eruption; again, such a unit may be difficult to delineate without considerable areal tracing.

Two kinds of units are essential elements of measured sections and any allied stratigraphic studies (Krumbein and Sloss, 1959). The more comprehensive kind is the formally identified and named rock division such as (in increasing rank) a member, formation, or group that can be recognized over a large area. These units are referred to as major subdivisions in stratigraphic work. In most situations they can be subdivided into various measurable units or subunits that constitute the basic division of the measured section. These basic units are not formally named, but are ordinarily numbered for convenient reference; for example, in a section measured near Bishop's Lodge and labeled *BL,* the units are numbered *BL*1, *BL*2, and so on, in upward succession from the base of the rock sequence.

How are the basic units chosen? Much of the choice is a matter of individual judgment and preference, and generally depends upon the scale and detail of the work. Typically it is based on recognizable features of lithology, and especially on changes, up or down section, in features such as composition, minor constituents, color, grain size, bedding, cross lamination, topographic expression, weathering characteristics, chert, concretions, fracturing, and fossils. Within a sequence composed of different rock types, as a series of alternating sandstones, shales, coals, and limestones, each unit ordinarily is chosen as one of different gross lithology from that of the rock immediately above and below. Where the beds are lithologically more homogeneous, separation can be made on the basis of features such as color, texture, structure, or other special features.

A sequence of limestones, for example, might be subdivided into measurable units according to color, types of grains, amount of chert, nature of bedding, and kinds of impurities present. Sandstones in sections commonly are divided into units on the basis of grain size, bedding,

CHOICE OF UNITS

cross lamination, color, mineralogy of the grains, and type of cement. Variations in color, minor constituents, bedding, and weathering characteristics are features typically used in subdividing thick shale sequences. Volcanic and layered intrusive rocks may be differentiated into units on the basis of rock type, color, mineral composition, texture, structures, inclusions, and weathering features. In addition to using features similar to those of sedimentary and igneous rocks, metamorphic rocks may be divided on metamorphic textures and structures, such as types of foliation and porphyroblastic structure.

In measuring sections for subsurface correlation, the units may be established as 5- or 10-foot divisions regardless of lithologic features. Samples from test holes and wells are collected, in most cases, by 5- or 10-foot intervals, hence the surface-section units can be mechanically matched with the subsurface sample control for ease in correlation. To simulate drill-hole cuttings, the outcrop samples can be broken in a small jaw crusher to about ⅛-inch fragments, which then can be compared side-by-side with normal well samples.

The purposes of measuring the section should have much to do with the thicknesses of subdivision units; if for detailed microfauna sampling, for example, thin units may need be chosen to give close control. On the other hand, if doing reconnaissance work over a large region, the geologist may be interested only in total thicknesses of major units, such as formations. In thick sections of similar rocks, such as alternating sandstones and shales, the clastic-rock beds may be lumped into thick measured units. However, key beds, marker beds, or economically valuable beds like a limestone, a distinctive sandstone, or a coal bed, may be set off as separate units, even if thin, because of their importance in areal correlation or their commercial value.

Basic measuring units in the thick uniform sequences may be for the most part, also thick and uniform. For example, in a rhyolitic welded tuff or ash flow that may be 400 feet thick, the natural units related to cooling may be: (1) basal, nonwelded zone, 20 feet thick, (2) partly welded zone, 40 feet, (3) densely welded zone, 100 feet, (4) upper partly welded zone, 200 feet, and (5) top, nonwelded zone, 40 feet thick.

GENERAL FIELD PROCEDURE

As indicated at the beginning of this chapter, section measuring can begin most effectively if it is based upon (1) a review of the geologic literature that describes the stratigraphic sequence, (2) use of available maps and vertical aerial photographs to locate promising exposures and to recognize lateral variations in the rocks, and (3) field reconnaissance to select the best sites for the measured sections.

The details of procedure in the field vary according to the techniques employed in establishing control as well as depend upon the relations between surface slope and inclination of the layered rocks. Surveying techniques are used to determine either (1) vertical difference in elevation and horizontal distance, as by plane-table or transit-tape traverses, or (2) slope distance and slope angle, using simpler instruments such as the Brunton compass, Jacob staff, and Abney hand level. Vertical

GENERAL FIELD PROCEDURE

and horizontal control can also be obtained from a topographic map, from surveying profiles (as for a tramway), and by using a combination of aerial photographs and an altimeter.

A fundamental question is whether to establish the surveying control for thickness determinations and to describe the rock units as an integrated, essentially simultaneous process, or to do these operations separately. The answer depends on the techniques used in measuring, the number of persons in the field party, and the purpose of measuring the section. For example, a two-man party plane-tabling a section ordinarily can work faster and more systematically if they set up the surveying control first and then return to describe the units and collect samples. Time would be lost if, for each unit, they switched from plane-tabling to describing and then back to plane-tabling. In contrast, a two-man party using the Jacob staff in most situations can move more swiftly by combining the two procedures—one man measuring with the Jacob staff while the other describes the units—rather than measuring the units and then retracing their steps to describe and sample the section.

Another decision is whether the rock units should be marked in the field. If measuring and describing are done separately, the units must be marked so that they can be described and sampled at any later time. Anyone then can return and easily review the measured section, and key beds can be traced laterally along the outcrops to observe any changes along the strike, without remeasuring the section or depending on only a recollection of exactly where the section was measured. Marking the units does take time, however, and if speed is of prime importance this part of the procedure may be eliminated. In all situations, however, at least one permanent mark should be made, probably at the first point of the section, so that the section can be reoccupied if necessary.

Field labeling of the units is here recommended, even for reconnaissance measuring. It can be done quickly and easily. Each boundary between units, in most instances a bedding plane, should be marked with a horizontal line, and the number of the unit (for example, $RC21$, $RC22$) should be indicated on the face of the rocks, preferably near the top of the unit. Where offsets in the line of section are made along prominent bedding surfaces or other horizons, arrows should be painted on the rocks showing the direction of offset of the section traverse.

Felt "pencils" of colored ink or paint may be employed for the marking of thin lines. For thick marks, a spray-paint can, pressure-type, can be used. Black roof-patching cement in small tubes makes excellent permanent marks on light-colored rocks. When running plane-table traverses, flags or strips of cloth may be more satisfactory than paint. Yellow, red, white, and orange, in about this order, are the colors that can be seen most easily, depending in part on the color of the rocks.

Using the one-man surveying instruments such as the Jacob staff and Brunton compass, a geologist can measure and describe a section without assistance. Under these conditions, a swift and thorough procedure is to measure and label with paint a sequence of about ten units, and then to retraverse the sequence in order to describe the rocks, collect samples, and search for fossils.

GENERAL FIELD PROCEDURE

An effectively functioning two-man team can do the work more than twice as rapidly as an individual, and probably with greater accuracy and thoroughness. If one person measured the units, labels them on the rocks, and checks strikes and dips, the other can simultaneously describe the lithology, collect any desired rock samples or fossils, and check for lateral variations in lithology. If numerous samples are to be collected, either a third person can be assigned to this work or the first geologist, after measuring a sequence of about ten units, can then return to aid in the collecting.

The surveying control process is more complicated, and it requires at least two persons for such techniques as plane-table and transit-tape traversing. For plane-tabling, the measured-section plot may be merely a skeleton of points, unit boundaries, and structural notes (strikes and dips, and faults), or part of a complete geologic and topographic map. The field party consists basically of an instrument man and a rod man; a third man may serve as a recorder to help the instrument man in keeping notes and calculating distances and elevations. The rod man, more often than the instrument man, needs an assistant when measuring a section, because, if the surveying and description of units are done simultaneously, he must not only occupy the control points with the rod, but also has to describe the lithology of the rock units, record strikes and dips, and collect samples. If a simultaneous procedure is followed, a three-man party is recommended: an instrument man, a geologist, and a geologic assistant. The surveying with the alidade and plane table is done by the instrument man, whereas the geologist and his assistant share placing the stadia rod, labeling the units with paint, taking strikes and dips, descriptions of the lithic units, and collecting rock samples and fossils.

In both cases, and especially when plane-tabling, trigonometric calculations may be necessary to determine the actual thicknesses of measured units. Simple computations, such as one- or two-step multiplication, can be done in the field, either with a slide rule or by using tables (see Appendix), but more complex calculations are commonly best made during the evenings at the office or in camp.

Descriptions of the rocks should be both written (hand lettered) and graphic. A field-sketched graphic section allows concise visual recording of much pertinent data and in some ways is superior to written descriptions or check lists in noting lithologic features, such as (among others) size, shape, and positioning of chert nodules, the irregularity or evenness of bedding planes, and variation of sedimentary, igneous, or metamorphic structures and textures. Fig. 2–7 is an example of a field-sketched graphic section (later redrafted) showing detailed lithologic features (Pray and Wray, 1963, page 210).

As suggested by Hayes (1909) and many others, emphasis in general field procedure should be placed upon organization, thoroughness, accuracy, and comprehensiveness. Above all, the investigator should be observant! The accuracy of measurements depends on correct observations of strikes and dips, lines of sight, level bubbles, scale readings, and of stadia rods. All mechanical details, especially arithmetic and plotting, should be double-checked. Thorough and comprehensive observation of

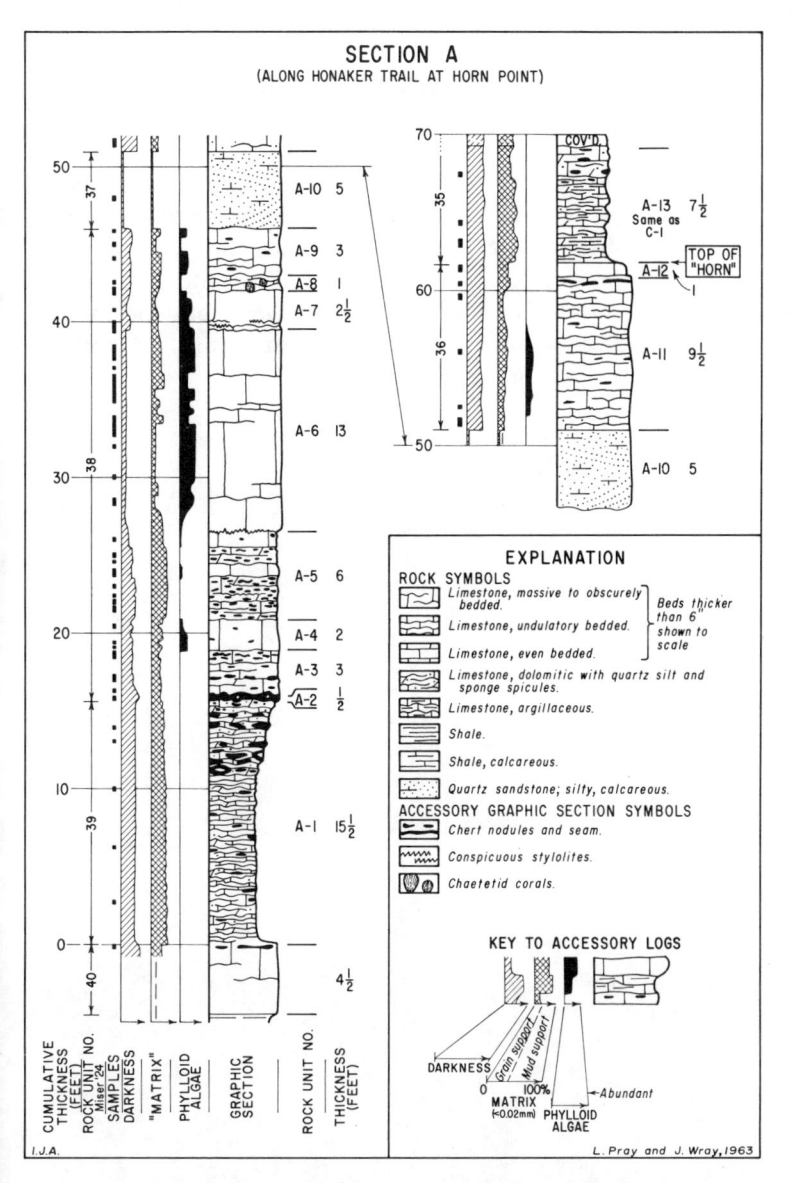

Fig. 2–7. Detailed field-sketched graphic section (redrafted) of Pennsylvanian rocks in southeastern Utah (Pray and Wray, 1963, page 210).

the rocks, both in the measured section and in its lateral extensions, is necessary to provide the maximum amount of useful data. However, the almost infinite amount of detail observable at each exposure demands a judicious summation of data (Proctor, 1961). Too much information certainly is better than not enough, but the most useful descriptions are limited to those features pertinent to the purpose of the work.

3 □ Techniques for Establishing Control

The selection of techniques and instruments for measuring stratigraphic sections depends upon:

1. the dip of the bedding or other layering, with the three general cases of dips horizontal or nearly so, dips vertical or nearly so, and dips within the broad intermediate range
2. the topography and its relation to attitude of the layering
3. how completely the rocks or other materials are exposed
4. the purpose of measuring the section as well as attendant degree of detail and accuracy that is desired
5. the amount and scale of lithologic variations in the sequence to be measured and studied
6. the number and experience of the personnel available
7. the amount of time available

The simplest and fastest methods and instruments that will yield reasonable accuracy should be used in any given situation.

DIRECT CONTACT MEASUREMENTS

Whether the units to be measured are horizontal, vertical, or inclined, their thickness can be determined directly by means of any linear scaling device held normal to both the dip and strike directions. Such measuring across exposed edges can be effected with the handle of a geologic pick that has been notched or otherwise marked off in tenths of a foot, a wood or metal yardstick, a 6-foot spring-rolled steel tape, a 6-foot wood or metal folding carpenter's rule, or with any other convenient linearly graduated device.

Direct measurement of thickness is most readily applicable to units that are thin, in general 5 or less feet thick. Thicker units also can be measured in this manner regardless of their attitude, but only if their surfaces of exposure are perpendicular to the surfaces bounding them from the adjacent units. A common example, caused by weathering and erosion of rocks along joints that are perpendicular to layering, is a thick horizontal bed that crops out as a vertical cliff. The thickness of such a bed, if less than 100 feet thick, can be measured directly with a 100-foot tape by weighting one end of the tape, lowering the weighted end to the bottom of the bed, and then reading the thickness on the tape at the top of the bed. Correspondingly, the thickness of a 100-foot vertical bed that crops out along a horizontal surface can be measured with a tape extended normal to the strike; if the surface slopes in the same direction as the strike of the vertical bed, contact measurements also can be made by placing the tape perpendicular to the strike, that is, along a horizontal line on the exposure.

JACOB-STAFF MEASUREMENTS

A Jacob staff is a lightweight pole, either solid or tubular and made either of wood or of metal, that is marked in graduations of feet and tenths of a foot. The minimum length should be about 5 feet, so that a clinometer placed on the top of the pole is at a comfortable height for direct reading. The maximum length is dictated by convenience of carrying in the field and by the observer's height. A wood or metal carpenter's rule, 6 feet long when unfolded, can be used in lieu of a rigid pole, but is rarely as satisfactory.

The Jacob staff is used to measure layered rocks directly on the outcrop; as the pole provides a steady support for a level or a clinometer, it permits hand-leveling with greater accuracy than that normally obtainable with free holding of the hand level or clinometer. Where beds or layers are well-exposed and where they intersect the surface at angles up to 50°, one geologist can quickly and accurately measure a detailed section with a Jacob staff. Under such conditions, this method becomes a prime choice for section measuring.

To measure a true stratigraphic thickness, the Jacob staff should be oriented normal to the surface of the beds by a clinometer. An Abney hand level, a Brunton compass, or a simple hand-made clinometer (Kummel, 1943) comprising a protractor and weighted pointer can be used. The Abney hand level (see Fig. 3-18) is easily held, gives an accurate line of sight, and is sturdy; the Brunton compass (see Fig. 3-21) is somewhat more cumbersome when used with the staff, and in general its clinometer is not as sensitive as that of the Abney level.

First, the dip of the units to be measured is determined. This dip value is set on the clinometer, which is then held against the top of the staff (Fig. 3–1). The base of the staff is placed on the base of the lowest unit of the sequence, and, as the geologist looks through the level in a direction perpendicular to the strike of the unit, he tilts the staff forward until the level bubble of the clinometer is centered; he is now sighting through the

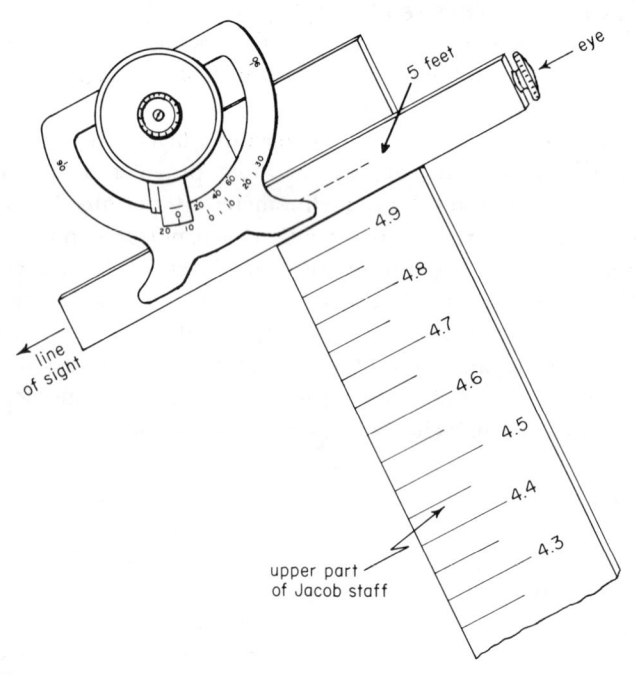

Fig. 3–1. Setting dip on clinometer of Abney hand level used with a Jacob staff.

JACOB-STAFF MEASUREMENTS

clinometer in a direction parallel to the dip of the beds. Thus the stratigraphic thickness of material between the base of the sequence and the point on the outcrop that is in his line of sight is measured directly on the Jacob staff; this is the distance between the base of the staff and the point where the hand level is held, or the top of a protractor if a simple clinometer is used, in this case the top mark on the staff (Fig. 3–2).

After the first staff-length is observed in terms of section thickness, the geologist moves up the outcrop, now placing the base of the staff on the point previously sighted and repeating the measurement procedures for the second "step" in the section. If the exposures are poor above the first "step," he can move parallel to the

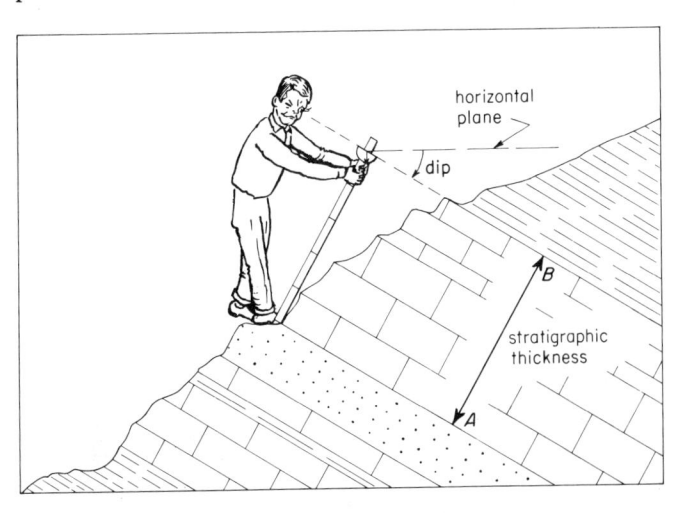

Fig. 3–2. Measuring stratigraphic thickness AB with a Jacob staff and simple clinometer.

layering to a new position at the same stratigraphic level (Fig. 3–3). Dips of the layering should be checked frequently as the work proceeds.

If the thickness of the unit to be measured is less than the full length of the Jacob staff, the unit is measured as outlined above, except that the clinometer is slid downward along the staff until the top surface of the unit is in the line of sight. The thickness of the measured unit then can be read directly from the graduation marking the position of the clinometer on the staff (Fig. 3–4). Where the combined thickness of two or more units is less than the total length of the staff, each of these thin units can be measured at one setting of the staff. If the

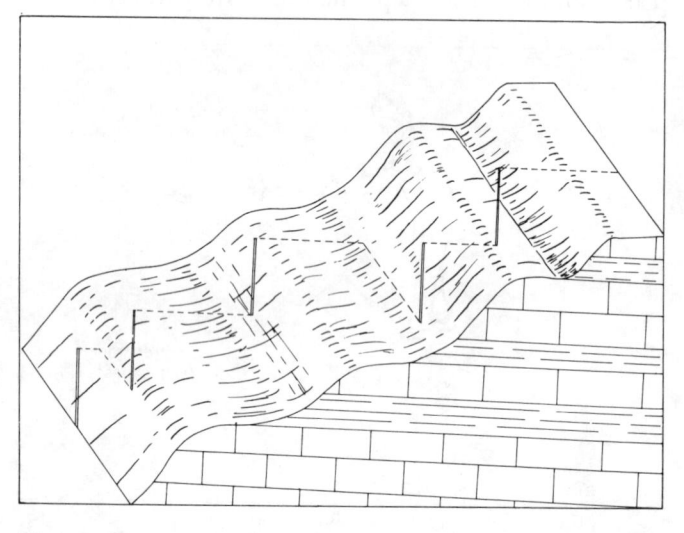

Fig. 3–3. Lateral offsets along bedding surfaces while measuring section with a Jacob staff.

JACOB-STAFF MEASUREMENTS

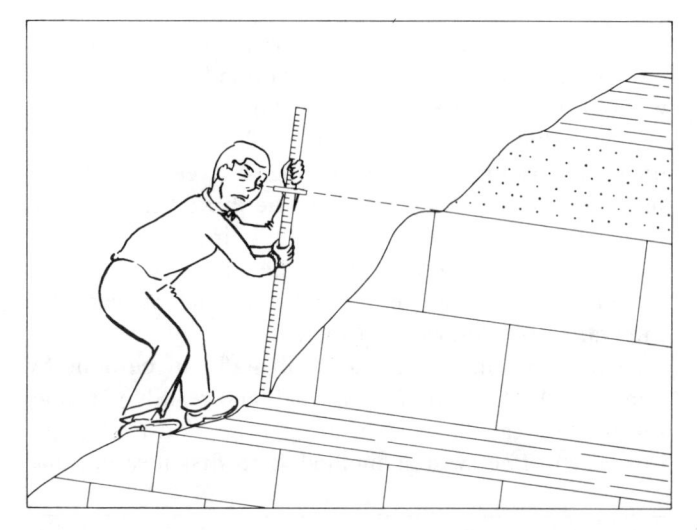

Fig. 3–4. Measuring unit with thickness less than length of Jacob staff.

lithic unit is thick, several full measurements of the staff, and perhaps a partial length of the staff, need to be used.

Where the beds are horizontal, the clinometer is used with a setting of zero, the Jacob staff is held vertical, and thickness is read directly as the difference in elevation from the base of the staff to the level line of sight. Under such conditions, a simple hand level can be used in place of a clinometer or a clinometer-equipped level. If the dips are 50° or more, it is difficult to hold the Jacob staff tilted exactly normal to the beds or layers, and hence other methods of measurement should be used.

66   TECHNIQUES FOR ESTABLISHING CONTROL

For beds dipping at angles of 10° to 30° and cropping out on fairly steep slopes, the Jacob staff can be utilized without a clinometer to obtain fairly satisfactory estimates of thickness. The geologist holds the staff perpendicular, by estimate, to the bedding or layering, and then sights in a direction parallel to the dip across a graduation on the staff, noting where his line of sight intersects the outcrop (Fig. 3–5). If the staff is held within 10° of the correct angle, the error in a 5-foot measured interval will be less than 0.1 foot.

Section measuring with a Jacob staff can be done by one man. As the equipment is small and readily portable, the method can be used in any terrain that a geologist can reach. The swiftest method is to first measure and

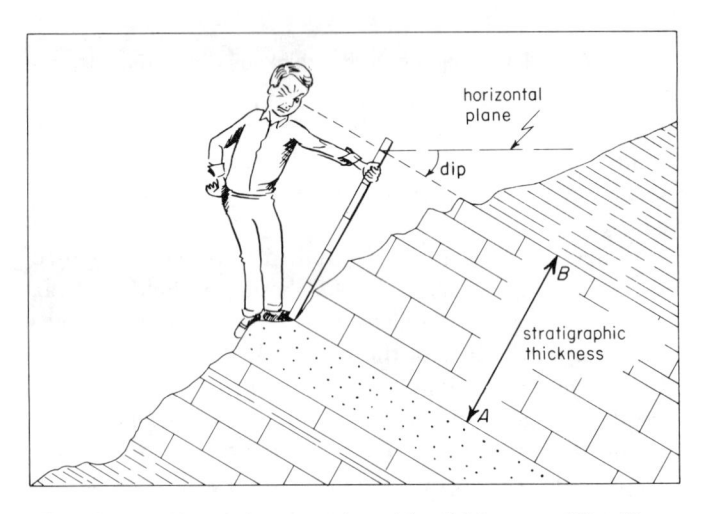

Fig. 3–5. Measuring stratigraphic thickness AB with a Jacob staff held normal, by estimation, to the bedding.

mark a sequence of about ten units, then come back to describe the lithology, collect rock samples, and hunt for fossils. A two-man party, however, can move at least twice as fast as an individual, as one man can measure the units and check dips while the second man describes the lithology and collects any desired rock samples or fossils. Even in reconnaissance work, it is wise to mark the units, as they then can be described and sampled sometime after they have been measured or anyone can return to check the section later.

Outcrops are rarely exposed in a straight upslope line, so offsets must be made, following along tops of units or along any sighted bedding plane (Fig. 3–3). Even if the units are plainly marked with paint, the line of the section must be described in detail in field notes, and its location noted on any available photographs and maps.

The Jacob staff is especially useful in the measuring of stratigraphic sections for subsurface control. To match the 5- or 10-foot intervals utilized in collecting cuttings from oil tests, 5-foot intervals can be measured directly with a 5-foot staff, and a representative rock sample or samples can be collected from each interval or pair of intervals. A section measured in this way is represented in Figs. 3–6 and 3–7, which include the field notes and the field-sketched columnar section. The 5-foot interval is also exceedingly useful for plotting the section in the field on graph paper.

The Jacob staff method for measuring sections has been used by geologists to a remarkably limited extent. This may be due in part to lack of recognition of its advantages and in part to an erroneous belief that the method is crude and inaccurate. Thus many geologists would not measure a section except with a plane table, alidade, and stadia rod, or with a tape and Brunton compass. Such methods, described further on, are more

SECTION Rhodes Canyon, San Andres Mts.   FORMATIONS   Yeso
LOCATION SE¼ sec.1, T. 12 S., R. 2 E.   BY F. Kott and R. Foster
COUNTY Sierra, N. Mex.   DATE 7/14/54

UNIT NO.	FEET	ROCK TYPE	COLOR, GRAINS, CEMENT, BEDS, STRUCTURES, WNG., TOPO., FOSSILS
Ry195	5	gyp	l.gy., fn-xl, 3-12" bds, rdd slope; scat. sts lam; St.N. 7° E., Dip 14° W.
Ry196a	4	"	"
Ry196b	1	sts,calc	l.gy., porous, mas-1' bds, wrs. l. brn slope
Ry197	5	"	"
Ry198a	2	"	"
Ry198b	3	Ls, sty.	gy, fn-xl, 1' bds, wrs smooth, ocng ledges Dip 11° W.
Ry199	5	"	"
Ry200	5	"	"
Ry201	5	sts,gypy	l.gy., fissile; gyp lam, partly covered; St.N. 10° E., Dip 12° W
Ry202	5	sts,calc.	l.gy., fissile; gyp, lam; wrs l. brn. slope
Ry203	5	Ls,sty	dk gy, fn-xl, ¼-4" bds, ocng ledges; Dip 14° W
Ry204	5	Sts,calc	l.gy. soft, 1' bds, rdd slope
Ry205a	3	"	"
Ry205b	2	gyp	gy, mottled; 3-9" bds; wrs mas, rdd ledges; Ls lam.
Ry206a	2	"	"
Ry206b	3	Ls,gypy	dk gy, fn-xl, ½-3" bds; ocng ledges; gyp lam; Dip 12° W.
Ry207	5	Ls	gy, fn-xl wi crs-xl, fetid, porous; 4-12" bds; Wrs. smooth dk gy ledges; scat. brachs, gastro, ostracods.
Ry208	5	"	"
Ry209a	1	sts,calc	l.gy, soft, 1" bds; slope
Ry209b	4	Ls.	gy-dk gy, fn-xl, fetid; 3-12" bds; wrs smooth dk.gy ledges
Ry210	5	"	" St. N. 9° E; Dip 14° W.

Fig. 3–6. Description of section measured with a Jacob staff in 5-foot units and partial units to be used as subsurface control. Representative samples were collected from each complete 5-foot unit, then RS 205 would contain, roughly, 60 percent siltstone and 40 percent gypsum.

sophisticated and can yield results somewhat more accurate than the Jacob-staff technique, but are much more costly and time-consuming, and are less readily adaptable to a wide variety of field conditions.

A considerable literature, summarized by Robinson (1959), describes variants and refinements of the Jacob-staff method. Walcott (1888), Hayes (1909), and Blackwelder (1913) presented original descriptions of the use of a staff with a clinometer compass, with an Abney level, and with a Brunton compass, and Kummel (1943) described a simple clinometer attached to a staff. Broggi (1946) analyzed the principles involved in Jacob-staff measurements, and outlined some applications to various outcrop situations. Bergstrom (1958) noted that the accuracy of measurements made by the staff method is limited, both by the accuracy of reading the level or clinometer and by the

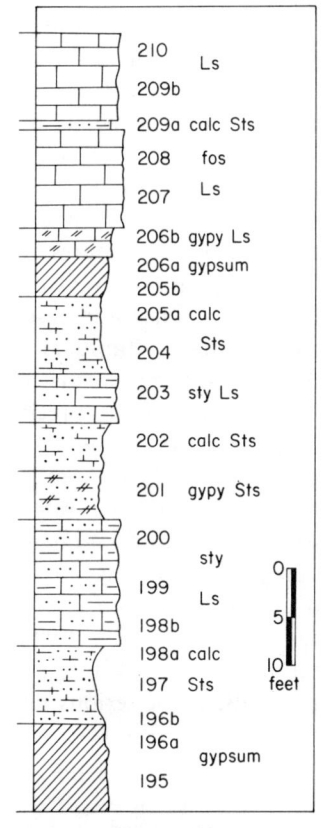

Fig. 3–7. Field-sketched columnar section described in Fig. 3–6. Measured with a Jacob staff.

sensitivity of these instruments. He compared vertical-angle sights made at the same target by 15 observers with Brunton compasses held on staffs, and found variations of more than a degree above and below the true angle as determined by a telescopic alidade. Bergstrom also developed a cylinder-type clinometer mounted directly on the Jacob staff; in using it, he obtained reproducibility within 15 minutes of arc.

As emphasized by Robinson (1959), work with the Jacob staff is fast and easy in nearly all field settings, the equipment is simple and inexpensive, no assistant is needed, no trigonometric calculations need be made, and the method can be precise, with results from different observers varying by less than 3 percent of the true thickness for the entire measured section. Other methods may yield more accurate results, but 3 percent is well within the normal range of accuracy in determining strike and dip of layered units. In comparison, the rate of change in thickness of some rock sequences is 20 percent or more within 1000 feet laterally. A large operator's error is possible, such as miscounting Jacob-staff intervals, or of serious cumulative error resulting from numerous small errors, in the same direction, from individual Jacob-staff steps. Thus some provision normally should be made for an independent check of the total thickness measured.

For long sights, 250 or more feet, the operator's error in reading vertical angles becomes significant. In practice, if many sights longer than 50 feet are required, other methods should be used; included among these are the tape and Brunton-compass method.

Measurements with the Jacob staff should be made at

right angles to the strike of strata wherever possible. As noted by Robinson (1959), true stratigraphic thickness can be obtained with the staff in traversing oblique to the strike if the clinometer is set at the apparent dip along the direction of traversing and sighting. This apparent dip may be measurable on the outcrop, or it can be determined from the strike, the dip, and the direction of traverse by using apparent-dip tables or nomograms (Lahee, 1961). As Threet (1962) pointed out, the direct measurement with the Jacob staff on a strike-oblique traverse, using the apparent dip, yields satisfactory results only for units with dips less than 18°, regardless of the direction of traverse, or for dips as large as 40°, if the traverse direction differs from the strike direction by at least 60°. These limitations are based on an expected error of less than 5 percent.

Hansen (1960) devised a special Jacob-staff assembly in which an Abney level can be slid up and down the staff or can be locked in any position. In addition, an auxiliary clinometer and spirit level is mounted normal to the Abney-level line of sight, so that the operator can tilt the staff sideways to determine directly the thicknesses of beds from sight lines parallel with their strike (Fig. 3–8). As Hansen noted, in hogback or cuesta ridges that flank many uplifts, the best exposures do not appear on the fronts or the backslopes of these ridges, but instead are found along the sides of water gaps or small valleys that in most places are cut normal to the strike. Owing to the presence of alluvium, across-strike measurements along the floors of these drainage ways are unfeasible, but along-strike sighting can be done on the valley walls.

Fig. 3–8. Jacob staff used to measure sections along the strike, right, and across the strike, left (modified from Hansen, 1960, fig. 1).

Broggi (1946) considered the use of the Jacob staff under all conceivable combinations of surface slope and attitude of layered rock units, and illustrated several unusual ways in which to measure the thickness of units. He restricted himself to traverses made normal to the strike of the strata.

Inclined beds that are exposed along a horizontal surface can be measured not only by sights in the down-dip direction, but also by sights in the against-the-dip direction, the clinometer setting being equivalent to the dip in either case (Fig. 3–9). The trick here is that any direct and reverse sights that make the same angle with the ground slope, intercept an equal distance along the slope, and therefore indicate the same thickness of beds. In the situation where the ground slope and dip of the

JACOB-STAFF MEASUREMENTS

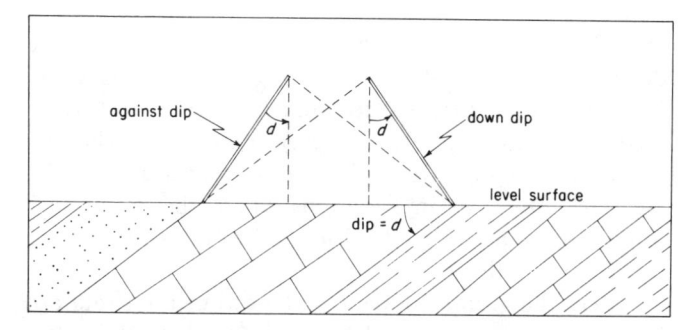

Fig. 3–9. Use of Jacob staff for down-dip and against-dip measurements of inclined beds along a horizontal surface.

strata are in the same direction but diverge downslope, and where the strata dip at angles greater than 45° (Fig. 3–10), the thickness can be measured in the "reverse" direction by holding the Jacob staff at a smaller

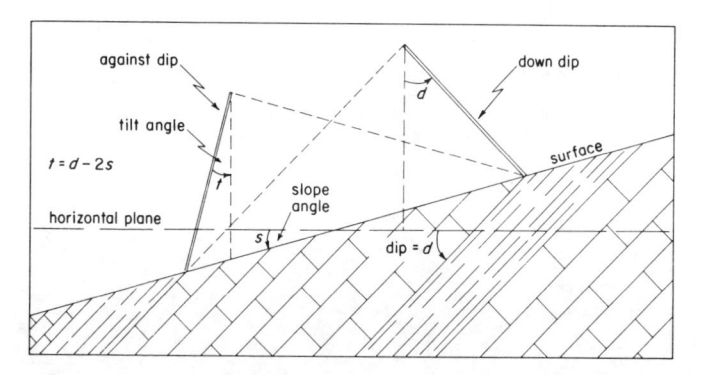

Fig. 3–10. Use of Jacob staff for down-dip and against-dip measurements of inclined beds along a surface sloping in the dip direction.

forward tilt than would be used for a traverse in the down-dip direction. The desired angle of tilt in this case is found from Broggi's formula: t (angle of tilt) = d (dip of beds) $-2s$ (slope angle). Thus the thicknesses of steeply dipping layered rocks can be measured in the "reverse" direction in situations where the Jacob staff could not be accurately held normal to the steep dips in the down-dip direction.

Where the ground slope and the dip of the strata are in opposite directions and they join at an angle of less than 90°, and where the strata dip steeply, measurements with the Jacob staff in the down-dip direction involve tilting of the staff to an impractical position. But reasonable angles of tilt are achieved if measurements are made in the reverse direction (Fig. 3–11). Broggi's formula for this case, $t = d - s$, fortuitously checks for the example given by him, but it is incorrect for general appli-

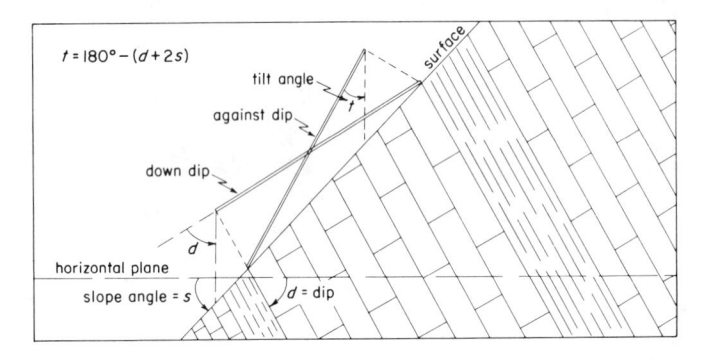

Fig. 3–11. Down-dip and against-dip measurements with Jacob staff of inclined beds along a slope dipping in opposite direction as the dip.

cation. Based on the geometry of similar triangles, the correct formula is $t = 180° - (d + 2s)$.

EYE-HEIGHT MEASUREMENTS

Eye-height measurements involve use of the observer's erect body as an ungraduated Jacob staff, the length of which is the vertical distance between the observer's eyes and the ground on which he stands. In contrast to the characteristic 5-foot length of the Jacob staff, eye height (and the corresponding measurement unit) varies from person to person and ordinarily is somewhat greater than 5 feet. Further, the human "staff" cannot be readily and reproducibly tilted to positions normal to dipping beds or other layers, so that a trigonometric correction must be made to determine true stratigraphic thickness. Eye-height measurements are easily and quickly made, and they have the advantage of requiring only a single sighting instrument. They can be made with a Brunton compass, which is normally carried for any type of field work, or with an Abney hand level. As with the Jacob staff, numerous offsets can be made along bedding surfaces in order to follow the best exposures upslope (Fig. 3–3).

If the units to be measured are essentially horizontal, there is no need for trigonometric corrections, the stratigraphic thickness merely being the difference in elevation between the base and top of the measured unit as determined by level lines of sight from a standing observer. An ordinary hand level or a telescopic (stadia) hand level can be used, as can an Abney hand level, or a Brunton compass with clinometer set at zero.

Locke Hand Level

The Locke hand level consists of a horizontal tube for sighting along a horizontal line, a small bubble tube mounted above the main tube, and an internal prism that provides a simultaneous view of the level bubble, the horizontal sighting cross hair, and the object sighted (Fig. 3–12). This simple and sensitive instrument is useful for measuring the thickness of horizontal layered rocks, as it serves for hand-leveling measurement of the difference in elevation between any two points.

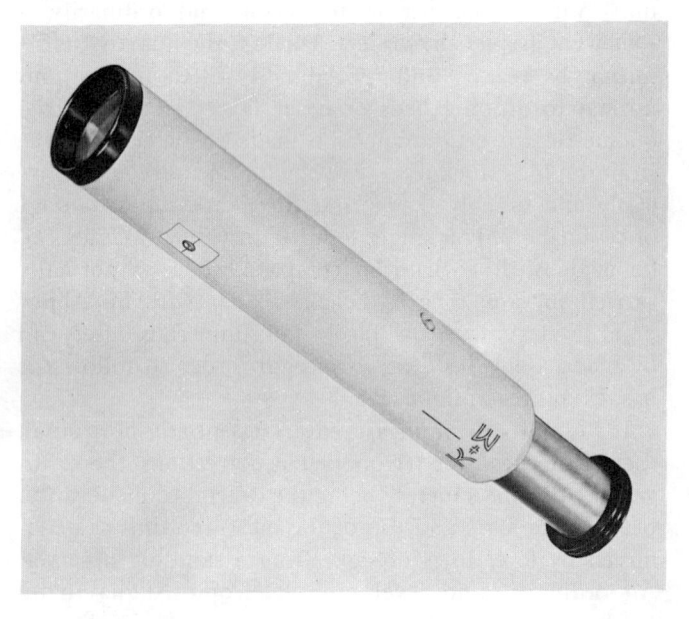

Fig. 3–12. Locke hand level, No. 800099. Courtesy of Keuffel & Esser Co.

EYE-HEIGHT MEASUREMENTS

Use of the Locke hand level is shown in Fig. 3–13. Here the thickness of the stratigraphic unit is AD; this is the sum of hand-leveled steps ab, $b'c$, and partial step $c'd$. The geologist stands erect on the base of unit AD at point a and, holding the instrument steadily in his hands, sights a level line to the ground point b'; the difference in elevation and the stratigraphic thickness of ab' are equal to the geologist's eye height, ab. Moving up to point b', the geologist relevels to ground point c'; the elevation difference leveled from a to c' is twice the eye height, or $2ab$. The horizontal distance from a to c' has no bearing on the stratigraphic thickness if the sight lines are level.

Occasionally, the thickness of the unit will be exactly equal to some number of complete hand-leveled steps,

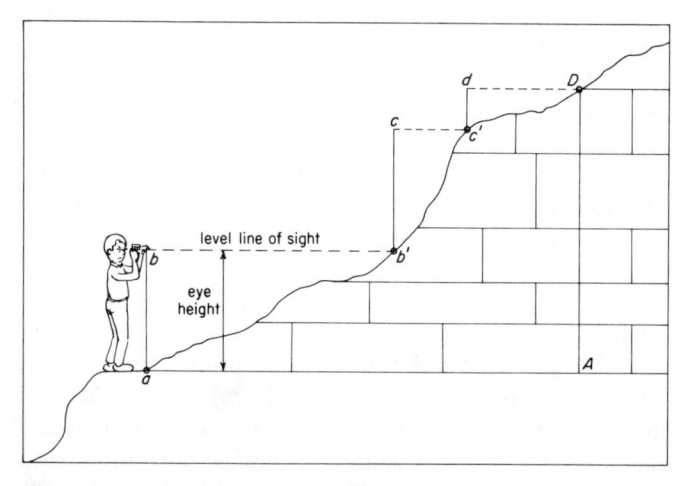

Fig. 3–13. Measuring thickness of horizontal beds with a hand level.

and hence will be equal to the eye height multiplied by the number of steps. In most cases, however, the measurement does not "come out even," and the uppermost step is a partial one ($c'd$ or $c'D$ in Fig. 3–13). Such partial steps can be measured directly by using supplemental devices such as: (1) a geologic pick with a foot and tenths of the foot marked on the handle, (2) a 6-foot spring-rolled steel tape with graduations in feet and tenths of a foot, (3) a wood or metal folding carpenter's rule, 6 feet long, or (4) a wood or metal yard stick.

If the partial step is exposed on a vertical face or corresponds to a series of ledges, it can be measured by placing a graduated pick handle against the exposure and measuring directly; 2.3 feet would be 2 full feet measured on two handle lengths plus 0.3 foot measured on the third handle length. If the partial step is on a slope, a 6-foot tape, carpenter's rule, or yard stick can be used as a Jacob staff, the geologist stooping down to sight a level line at the top of the partial step (Fig. 3–4). If the partial step is only slightly less than a full eye-height step, the top line of sight at eye height can be directed to the outcrop, the target point noted, and the distance then measured vertically downward to the top of the stratigraphic unit; this distance is subtracted from the eye height to obtain the true thickness of the partial step.

Using only a hand level or a Brunton compass with clinometer set at zero, a graduated geologic pick handle, and a 6-foot rolled tape, a geologist can easily measure most sections of horizontal or nearly horizontal rock units. The level method can be used without appreciable error only for units with dips of less than one degree,

EYE-HEIGHT MEASUREMENTS

and then only if the leveling is up a steep slope. The error, for example, in leveling up a 45° slope on beds dipping 2° into the hill will be 4 percent, that is, 0.2 foot in 5 feet.

A section measured with the Locke hand level and a 6-foot tape is represented in Figs. 3–14 and 3–15 in the form of field notes and a field-sketched column. The

SECTION Commadore strip pit
LOCATION SW¼ sec. 2, T. 9 N., R. 6 W.
COUNTY Owen, Ind.

FORMATIONS Brazil p. 42
BY F. Kottlowski
DATE 6/27/49

UNIT NO.	FEET	ROCK TYPE	COLOR, GRAINS, CEMENT, BEDS, STRUCTURES, WNG., TOPO., FOSSILS, R.S.
Cb1	16.0	Sh,sy	mostly cov. below water to top of Upper Block Coal
Cb2	6.1	Sh,sy	l.gy–dk.gy, mic, wrs. l.bn; thn. ss lam.; thn. coal lam. nr top
Cb3	0.2	Ss,calc.	gy, fn-grd, thn-bdd, lent., concy
Cb4	1.4	Sh,cly	dk gy, thn undulat bdng, wrs l. gy; coal lam.
Cb5	1.1	coal	blk, semi-block, much vitrain; ledge; 2 Joint sets St. N. 10°W. and N. 74°E.; RS49-212 Minshall Coal
Cb6	0.3	Sh,carb	blk, paper-thn. lam, much marcasite
Cb7	3.4	Sh,carb	blk, sheety; mas., forms large blocks along joints; slope
Cb8	3.9	Sh	gy, platy, wrs. gy bn to small nodules; slope
Cb9	0.6	Sh,calc.	gy; knobby calc. conc, fos., ledge
Cb10	3.3	Sh,calc.	dk gy. soft, fos., slope
Cb11	3.5	Ls,arg	bn-blu, sw sy; grades lat to calc. sts; ledge; many brachs
Cb12	1.0	Sh,calc	gy–dk gy-blu gy, soft. fos. slope, fissile
Cb13	1.3	sts,calc	l. gy;± sy thin-bdd, ledge; many brachs
Cb14	2.4	Ls	gy-blu gy, med-xl, one thk. bd., wrs red-bn; many crin, fusys, brachs; glauconite, oolites. RS49-213 FS 49-14
Cb15	9.4+	Ss	l.bn, fn-med grd, thn bdd, wrs bn ledges; basal 0.2' calc, fos.= Ls soil? RS49-214 nr center. Grades up into sy soil.

Fig. 3–14. Description of section measured with a Locke hand level and 6-foot tape.

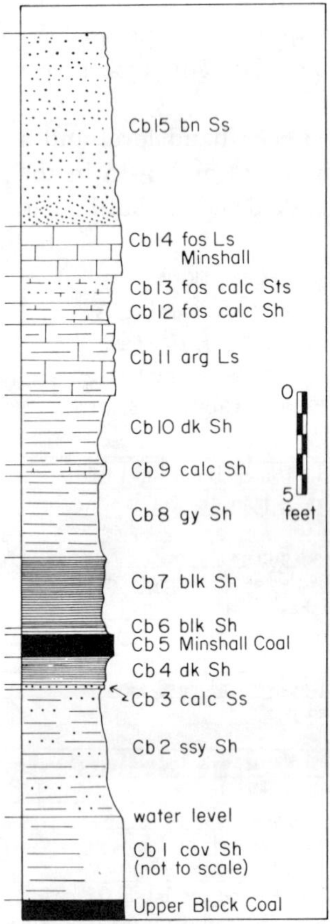
Cb 15 bn Ss
Cb 14 fos Ls
Minshall
Cb 13 fos calc Sts
Cb 12 fos calc Sh
Cb 11 arg Ls
Cb 10 dk Sh
Cb 9 calc Sh
Cb 8 gy Sh
0
5
feet
Cb 7 blk Sh
Cb 6 blk Sh
Cb 5 Minshall Coal
Cb 4 dk Sh
Cb 3 calc Ss
Cb 2 ssy Sh
water level
Cb 1 cov Sh
(not to scale)
Upper Block Coal

Fig. 3–15. Field-sketched columnar section described in Fig. 3–14.

beds are of Pennsylvanian age, crop out in southwestern Indiana, dip about 40 feet per mile, and are exposed in the steeply sloping walls of a coal-strip pit (Fig. 2–4). Numerous units thinner than the 5.3-foot eye height necessitated direct measurements with a steel tape. Most of the resistant beds crop out as ledges, so that thicknesses were taped directly on their exposed edges.

Telescopic Hand Level

A telescopic (stadia) hand level comprises a prism-projected level bubble, a single horizontal cross hair, a set of adjacent horizontal stadia hairs as in a telescopic alidade, and a system of lenses for use of the instrument as a low-power telescope. In measuring the thickness of horizontal beds, it is employed directly as a hand level, with the middle hair establishing the level line.

As in a telescopic alidade, the target interval appearing

EYE-HEIGHT MEASUREMENTS

between the upper and lower stadia hairs (Fig. 3–16) is proportional to the distance of the target from the instrument in the ratio of 1:100. At a distance of 300 feet, for example, the exposed top and bottom of a horizontal 3-foot bed will appear exactly along the top and bottom hairs when sighted, if the bed crops out at the same general elevation as the instrument. Unless used only as a hand level, the distance to the target point must be known, and then the telescopic hand level can be employed as a crude, rapidly handled alidade. The distance can be determined either by an intercept on a stadia rod (distance equals the intercept multiplied by 100 for a level sight), or by taping, by pacing, or by scaling from an accurate map or from a photograph with known scale. The difference in elevation from the instrument, when it is leveled, to the target can be read directly from a stadia rod, or it can be calculated from the distance and grade.

The grade is the elevation difference per 100 feet expressed as a percentage; thus a 9-foot elevation difference along a 150-foot traverse represents an average grade of 6 percent. The total interval between the lines of sight corresponding to the upper and lower stadia hairs of the telescopic hand level is one grade percent, and each of these sight lines is one-half grade percent from the line of sight marked by the middle, level hair.

The grade can be determined with the stadia hairs by the interval-step method (Low, 1957, page 137). As shown in Fig. 3–16, to find the grade to a point x above the level line and out of the field of level sight, first level the telescope and select a small, readily identified object point that is crossed by the upper stadia hair (a in Step

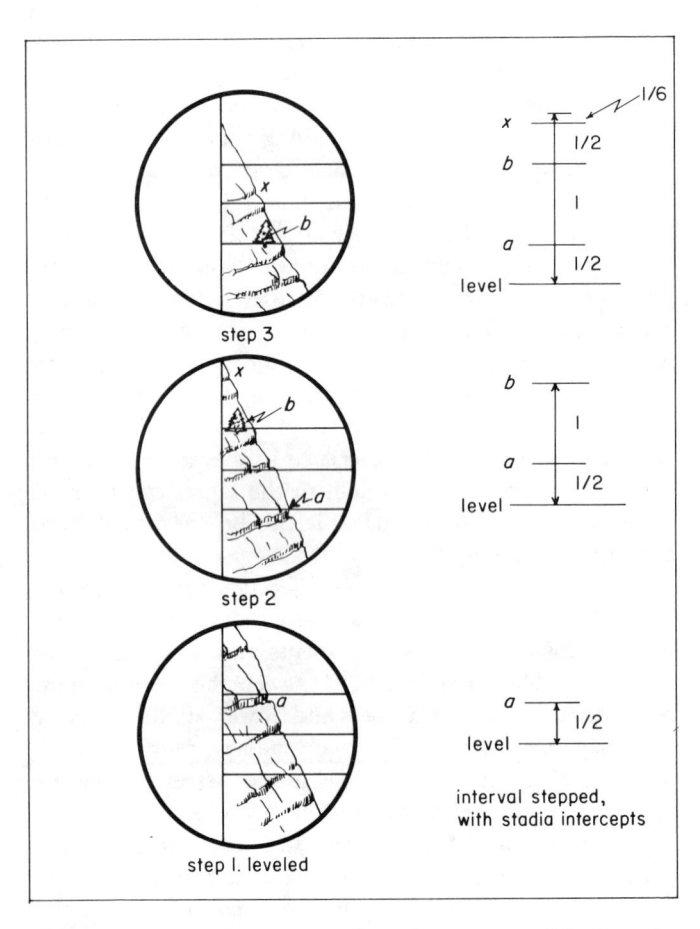

Fig. 3–16. Determination of grade percent with the telescopic hand level by the interval-step method.

EYE-HEIGHT MEASUREMENTS

1). Then move the telescope upward until the lower stadia hair is on this same object (Step 2). As point x is still above the upper stadia hair in the illustrated example, select another object point b that is crossed by the upper hair, and then direct the telescope upward once more until the lower hair is on b (Step 3). After this step, x is one-third of the interval from the center hair to the upper stadia hair, therefore the grade from the original level line to x is the sum of ½ + 1 + ½ + ⅙ intercepts. This is 2⅙, which is equal to a grade of 2⅙ percent. If the horizontal distance to point x is 200 feet, the difference in elevation is 2⅙ percent times 200, or 4⅓ feet.

If not utilized as a simple hand level, the telescopic hand level is useful for measuring sections only where gently dipping beds are being measured up a low-angle slope and where the rock layers dip into the slope (Fig. 3–17). The grade from A to B is determined (sighting from A to a point that is, by estimation, eye height above B) and converted into an angle a; the conversion may be read directly from the two scales (percent grade and elevation angle scales) on the Brunton compass and on the Abney hand level. Alternatively it can be calculated from natural tangent tables, the grade percent being 100 times the tangent of the elevation angle. For example, a grade percent of 8.75 divided by 100 is 0.0875, the tangent of 5°.

The grade angle a is added to the dip angle d, equaling the sum angle s. After pacing or taping the slope distance AB, the thickness CB is calculated from the formula $CB = AB \sin s$.

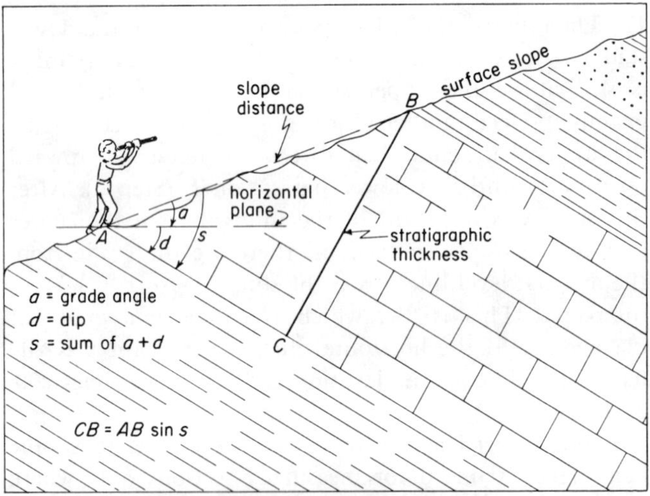
slope distance
surface slope
B
horizontal plane
a
d
s
A
stratigraphic thickness
C
a = grade angle
d = dip
s = sum of a + d
CB = AB sin s

Fig. 3–17. Measurement of gently dipping beds with telescopic hand level.

In the special case of horizontal beds, the thickness can be measured either by hand-leveling or by determining the grade and distance and then computing the difference in elevation as the product of percent grade times distance.

The telescopic hand level is much more easily portable but much less accurate than a tripod-mounted telescopic alidade. The alidade is preferable whenever there is a reasonable choice between the two instruments. A Jacob staff is more accurate, more easily handled, and better adapted for measurements with most combinations of dips and slopes than the telescopic hand level.

Abney Hand Level

The Abney hand level (Fig. 3–18) is a straight metal tube about 5 inches long and ½ inch square that is equipped with a graduated vertical angle arc and rotating arc level assembly. The arc can be set on either of two scales, an upper one of grade percent, and a lower scale of degrees. With the arc set at zero, the Abney level can be used for horizontal sights; thus it is interchangeable with the Locke level for directly measuring the thickness of horizontal beds by eye-height hand-leveling.

Inclined beds can be measured with an Abney hand level using the method outlined by Hewett (1920, pages 382–384). The geologist first determines the dip of the

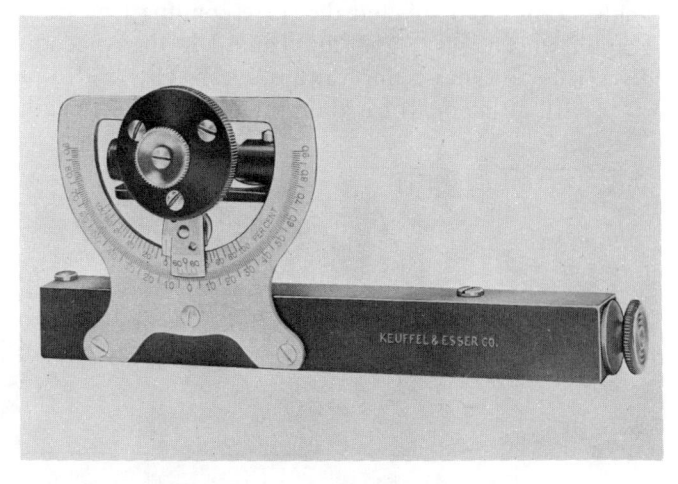

Fig. 3–18. Abney hand level, No. 800154. Courtesy of Keuffel & Esser Co.

beds to be measured and then sets the level at this dip value on the vertical angle arc; the dip should be checked within thick units and for every thin unit, so that the level setting is changed whenever necessary. As shown in Fig. 3–19, the geologist stands at the base of the unit and sights in the direction perpendicular to the strike, or in the direction of apparent dip if the section is measured oblique to the strike. He observes a point on the outcrop that is in the line of sight inclined at the dip angle; this is the inclined sight line established by leveling the bubble while looking through the instrument. The stratigraphic thickness is then equal to the eye height times the cosine of the dip angle ($AB = AC \cos a$). When one uses this method frequently, he should prepare a table for field use listing, for his eye height, dip angles from 0° to 50° and the corresponding true stratigraphic thicknesses (Fig. 3–20). Table 1 in the Appendix gives true thicknesses for various eye heights and dips.

As with all methods based on intervals of fixed length,

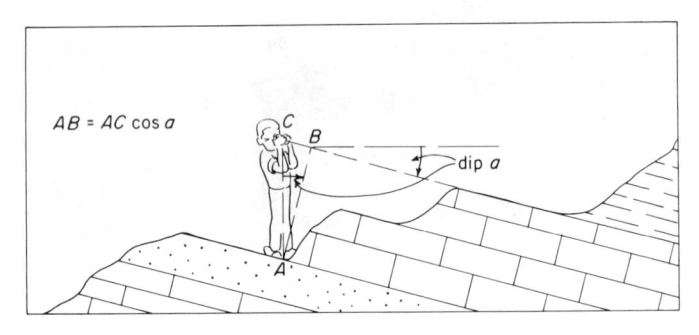

Fig. 3–19. Hewett method: measuring the thickness of a unit with a clinometer set at the angle of dip.

EYE-HEIGHT MEASUREMENTS

dip	$eh \times \cos$ dip	dip	$eh \times \cos$ dip
0	5.30	26	4.76
1	5.30	27	4.72
2	5.29	28	4.68
3	5.29	29	4.64
4	5.29	30	4.59
5	5.28	31	4.54
6	5.27	32	4.49
7	5.26	33	4.44
8	5.25	34	4.39
9	5.23	35	4.34
10	5.22	36	4.29

Fig. 3–20. Table correcting eye-height measurements for dip using Hewett method. Eye height, eh, is 5.3 feet.

the problem of partial intervals is encountered with any measured unit whose thickness does not correspond to eye-height length or to a multiple thereof. A graduated geologic pick handle, steel tape, or rule can be used to measure directly those thicknesses that are less than eye height. The 6-foot folding carpenter's rule is relatively firm when unfolded, and hence can be used as a Jacob staff by tilting it forward normal to the dip for downward sighting along the dip direction. A 6-foot, spring-rolled steel tape is more easily carried, but is much more flexible and hence must be handled with care when used as a staff, especially if the dip is more than 10°. The geologic pick handle, slightly more than a foot long, is too short for most partial eye-height measurements.

As shown in Figs. 3–13 and 3–19, irregularities in the ground surface have no bearing on the measurements or calculations involved in determining stratigraphic thickness. However, the Hewett method is not accurate when traversing on a long dip slope because irregularities in the attitude of the layered rocks over such an extensive surface make it almost impossible to obtain an accurate average dip and strike. Also, any angular sighting errors cause greater thickness errors if the line of sight is long (more than 50 feet) rather than if it is short.

The geologist should always assume the same posture in order that his eye height does not vary from one interval to the next. When sighting, he should set his feet fairly close together and center their length and width over the occupied point to place his eye directly above the ground point. He should take particular care in identifying and then moving up to occupy the line-of-sight point observed to begin the next step. If this point is at the base of a poorly exposed sequence, he may find it desirable to move laterally along the plane intersected by the point (Fig. 3–3). The method is not accurate when the dips are greater than 60°, owing chiefly to the effect of an error's being larger for high dips.

Brunton Compass

The Brunton pocket transit, called the Brunton compass by most geologists, includes a compass, sighting mirror, universal level and vertical-angle level, sighting arm and peep sights, and two scales for reading vertical angles, one in percent grade and one in degrees (Fig. 3–21). The Brunton compass is the all-purpose instrument of the

EYE-HEIGHT MEASUREMENTS

field geologist and is so necessary in most field work that it has become a symbol of the profession. A small, compact, sturdy instrument, it is easily carried in a leather case fastened to one's belt or placed in a pocket. When used, it can be hand-held or mounted on a small tripod. It is sensitive, reliable, and versatile, and can be used, for example, as a hand level, a clinometer, an alidade, and a hand transit, as well as a surveyor's compass. The Brunton compass is the sole instrument for some field procedures, and it also can be used to supplement other instruments, such as the plane table and telescopic alidade, when utilized to level a plane table or plumb a stadia rod.

In the measuring of sections, the Brunton compass is widely employed to obtain strikes and dips (Low, 1957; Compton, 1962; Lahee, 1961), as a hand level or a cli-

Fig. 3–21. Brunton compass, No. 800020. Courtesy of Keuffel & Esser Co.

nometer for determinations normal to the strike, and as a compass and clinometer for measurements oblique to the strike. The Hewett method of eye-height measurements, as previously described in terms of using an Abney hand level, was originally conceived for application of the Brunton compass. The Abney level is slightly more sensitive and accurate for section measuring but it is not as versatile an instrument as the Brunton compass; even when the Abney hand level is used, the strikes and dips of the measured layers must be obtained by means of a Brunton or some similar compass.

In measuring the thickness of horizontal strata, the Brunton compass is converted into a hand level, the vertical or clinometer arc being set at zero and the compass held on edge. The geologist looks through the peep sight along the sighting arm, simultaneously centering the level bubble and observing the leveled target point. The bubble is observed in the mirror of the compass during this procedure. When measuring inclined beds by the Hewett method, the vertical arc of the Brunton clinometer is set at the angle of the dip; sighting in a line normal to the strike, the geologist then notes a point on the ground that is in his line of sight as inclined at the dip angle (Fig. 3–22). The thickness of the unit is calculated, as noted earlier, according to the equation $AB = AC \cos a$.

This is the *most practical method* of section measuring for one person who concurrently is engaged in other field work. The Brunton compass, a short tape or 6-foot folding rule, and the normal field notebook are the only necessary items of equipment.

After measuring many sections, Hewett (1920, page

EYE-HEIGHT MEASUREMENTS

384) noted that the sums of thicknesses, as determined through use of the Brunton compass, were in most instances within 5 percent of the thicknesses more accurately measured by means of the telescopic alidade and stadia rod. As indicated by Threet (1962), the Brunton compass can be used on traverses oriented oblique to the strike of the measured units. Calculations are made according to the formula given in the preceding paragraph, but a is now the angle of apparent dip, that is, the component of dip in the direction of the traverse. The Brunton compass clinometer is set at this angle in making the observations. This apparent dip may be measured at the outcrop, or it can be calculated by means of graphic computers (Satin, 1960; Threet, 1957), apparent-dip tables, or nomograms using the dip angle, direction of dip, and direction of the traverse.

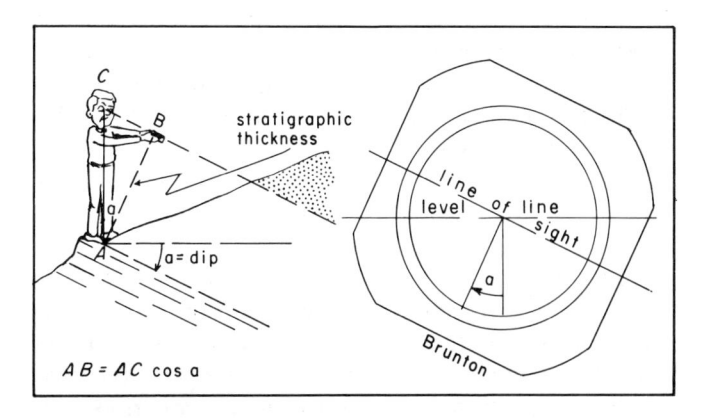

Fig. 3–22. Measuring thickness of an inclined unit AB with Brunton compass by the Hewett method.

PLANE TABLE AND TELESCOPIC ALIDADE TECHNIQUES

The plane table and telescopic alidade can be used to determine the location of a measured section and the positions of the units within that section. By means of these two instruments plus a stadia rod, the direction and the distance are determined from one point to another, along with the difference in elevation between the two points. This is a basic technique for establishing control in geologic mapping, and its application to the measuring of sections involves merely a shift in emphasis. Indeed, the measurements may constitute part of the control for a complete map that includes the line of section along with geology, topography, drainage, and cultural features. In most instances, however, the measured section "map" is little more than a strip comprising a skeleton of instrument stations, stadia rod points, and traverse lines, along with contacts and structural features of the measured beds. Detailed description of plane-table control techniques is beyond the scope of this manual; thorough treatment of this general topic is already available in the published literature (for example, Low, 1952, 1957; Compton, 1962; Forrester, 1946).

The simplest type of alidade is a metal ruler on which folding sights are mounted at each end to give a sighting line parallel to the ruler's edge. This open-sight or peep-sight alidade is used on a traverse board, generally 15 inches square, that is mounted on a light tripod and can be either rotated freely in a plane or locked in position. The board can be leveled by adjusting the legs of the tripod until the universal level ("bull's-eye" level) of a Brunton compass placed flat on the board shows a centered bubble. A piece of drawing paper or a map is fastened to the board to be used in plotting control data for the section.

The alidade and board are placed over a starting instrument station within the area of the section to be measured. Where possible the point should be chosen so that the entire section can be "shot in" without moving the board to another station. In most situations, however, more than one instrument station is necessary; these need not lie directly along the line of the measured section, nor need all of them be off to the same side of this line. Errors are minimized when each instrument station is vertically about midway between the highest and lowest points of that part of the section controlled from the station.

A point is marked on the drawing paper to represent the initial instrument station (point 1 in Fig. 3–23). The board is oriented with respect to north either by compass or by a line of sight to a prominent second point whose location is known relative to point 1. When orienting by compass, a Brunton compass is laid parallel to a north line drawn on the paper and the board rotated until the compass needle points north, the line then being oriented north-south. Or, a second known point 2 may be sighted, its distance and direction from point 1 plotted, the alidade edge placed on the line connecting points 1 and 2, the board oriented, and then fastened in place. Known point 2 may be a stream intersection,

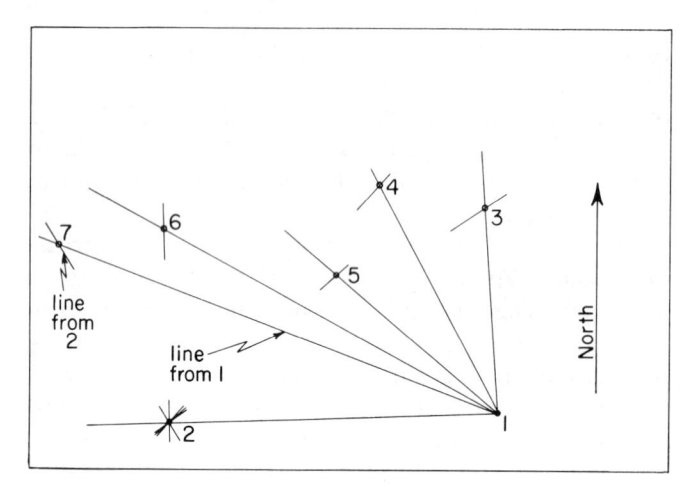

Fig. 3–23. Points located with an open-sight alidade by intersection as drawn on the traverse-board sheet.

bench mark, hilltop, or any similar prominent point whose distance and direction from point 1 are known from a map, photograph, or by direct measurements.

New points can be located by intersection of lines from two known points or by determining the direction and distance from a known, located point. For intersection while station 1 is occupied, draw pencil lines (Fig. 3–23) from point 1 along lines of sight toward points 3 through 7, which are at the base of section units being measured. Station 2 is then occupied, the traverse table is oriented by sighting back to station 1 with the alidade edge placed on the line connecting points 1 and 2. Then sighting at points 3 through 7, pencil lines are drawn from point 2 to intersect the lines from point 1; the intersections of the lines mark the locations of points 3 through 7. These latter points must be easily observed and recognized from both stations 1 and 2; if necessary, they can be marked by paint or cloth flags. The intersection angle of the lines of sight from stations 1 and 2 should be greater than 30° to accurately locate the point of intersection; if the angle is less than 30°, the intersection of the lines may be a broad point or even a short line when drawn on the plotting paper.

New ground points can be located on the plotted map by determining the direction and distance from occupied stations. In this method, having the board oriented with respect to north, the alidade ruler is placed with its edge on point 1 and then is lined up with point 3; the line of sight is then drawn on the map. The distance to point 3 must be measured, as by pacing or taping, and it is scaled off from point 1 along the line drawn on the map. If the altitude of point 3 differs from that of point 1, the difference can be determined by measuring the vertical angle of the line of sight using the Brunton compass or Abney level, followed by either a graphic plot or simple trigonometric calculation involving the measured distance between the two points and the vertical angle. The paced or taped distance then is corrected to a horizontal, map distance either from the graphic plot or by a trigonometric computation.

The open-sight alidade and traverse board method has the advantages of speed and portability, hence is a good reconnaissance method giving surprisingly accurate results when the work is done carefully.

The telescopic alidade is an instrument for measuring distances by stadia and for plotting lines of sight along the fiducial edge of the base. An operator can obtain precise results with this instrument; for most purposes of section measurement a relatively simple plane-table traverse is sufficiently accurate. Instrument stations may be as much as 750 feet apart with stadia rod points occupied wherever needed, principally at the base of units to be measured, at points marking changes in dip, and at breaks in the topography. In areas of low relief and where beds dip at low angles, the measurements cover long horizontal distances as compared with thicknesses of the units, so that considerable care must be taken to avoid errors especially those in vertical measurements. In this instance, errors in vertical measurements cause large errors in thicknesses.

A telescopic alidade consists of a 12- to 32-power telescope with cross hairs and stadia hairs mounted in the focal plane of the optical system, levels for trimming the instrument, scales for measuring vertical angles when the telescope is inclined upward or downward and for converting slope distances to horizontal distances, and a magnetic needle for orienting by magnetic bearings, all mounted on a flat base with a straight beveled edge, the fiducial edge, which is parallel to the line of sight of the telescope. Most telescopic alidades have a vertical cross hair, horizontal cross hair, upper and lower stadia hairs, and a lower "¼" stadia hair placed halfway between the central horizontal cross hair and the lower stadia hair.

The two common types of telescopic alidades are the explorer's alidade and the topographer's alidade. The telescope of the latter (Fig. 3–24) is mounted on a pedestal that extends about 8 inches upward from a base 15 inches long. The explorer's alidade is several

PLANE TABLE AND TELESCOPIC ALIDADE

inches lower, and thus is more compact; however, its low-mounted telescope, to be read accurately, can be elevated and depressed only about 15° from level.

Directions drawn along the fiducial edge and distances determined by stadia are plotted on a map sheet that is fastened to a plane-table board. The most common board sizes are 24 × 31 inches, 18 × 24 inches, and 15 × 22 inches. The telescopic alidade is too large and heavy to be handled effectively on the light traverse boards mentioned earlier. The plane table is usually mounted on a tripod that has a special ball-and-socket head, so that the board can be tilted until it is level, locked in this leveled position, and then rotated about a vertical axis to any

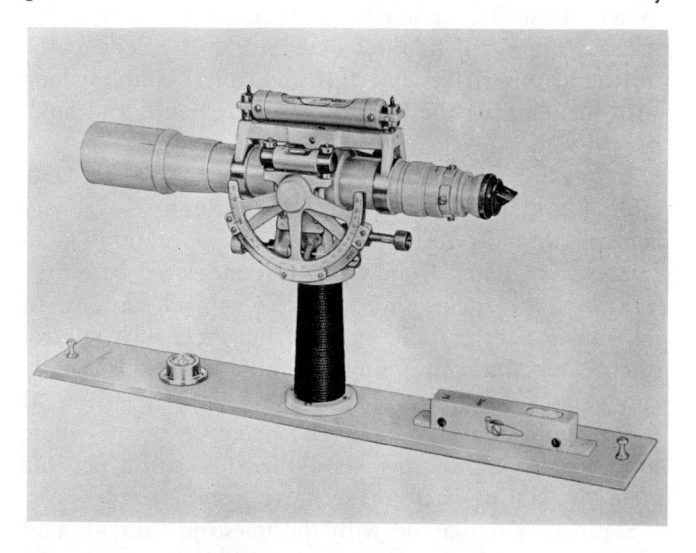

Fig. 3–24. Topographic telescopic alidade, No. 760020 Paragon. Courtesy of Keuffel & Esser Co.

desired orientation. A stadia rod is employed to determine distances. Many varieties of these rods are available, and in general they should be rugged but light in weight, 10 to 13 feet long when opened out or otherwise fully extended, and plainly and accurately graduated in feet and tenths of a foot.

A plane-tabling party ordinarily consists of at least two persons, an instrument man who operates the alidade on the tripod-mounted plane table, and a rodman who holds the stadia rod on points whose locations are to be determined. If the rodman can move swiftly from point to point, the instrument man may need assistance in recording his readings and making his calculations. When measuring sections, it is the rodman who generally needs assistance if he must describe the lithology of the units, measure strikes and dips, and collect samples along with his selecting the location of stadia points and holding the rod.

In making a geologic or topographic map, a plane-table party usually begins by establishing its primary control, in most instances a network of stations accurately triangulated from a carefully measured base line. Traverses are then run from these control stations. In measuring stratigraphic sections, however, such control often is too time-consuming. A simple traverse is usually run along or near the line of the measured section. If possible, this traverse should be tied into points whose locations are known, or it should be checked for possible errors by closing back to the starting station.

Sighting a stadia rod with the telescopic alidade and reading the distance intercepted on the rod between the two stadia hairs, the operator can determine the distance

PLANE TABLE AND TELESCOPIC ALIDADE 99

between the alidade and the rod, as well as the difference in their altitudes. The alidade is so designed that the intercept of the upper and lower stadia hairs on the rod, as it is viewed through the telescope, is $\frac{1}{100}$ of the distance between the alidade and the target if the rod is held perpendicular to the line of sight. For level lines of sight, distance thus is simply the rod intercept multiplied by 100, or $R.I. \times 100$.

Inasmuch as the rod customarily is held in a vertical position, the rod intercept must be corrected for inclined lines of sight through a conversion to what the intercept would be if the rod were rotated to a position normal to the line of sight, that is, a conversion of AB to AC in Fig. 3–25. As shown in the figure, $AC = AB \cos a$, where a is the vertical angle of sight read from the alidade. Thus the slope distance $S = AB \cos a \times 100$. But S is a *slope* distance for all inclined lines of sight, and hence must be converted to *horizontal* distance H for

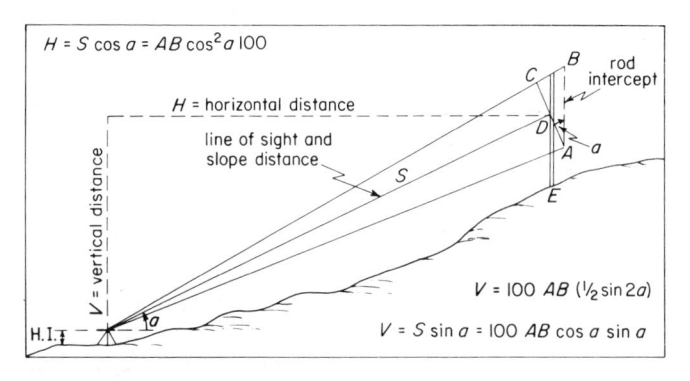

Fig. 3–25. Trigonometric relations of stadia intercept corrections.

plotting on the map, which is a projection to a horizontal plane. Because $H = S \cos a$, it can be calculated from the formula $H = AB \cos^2 a \times 100$, where AB is the intercept read on a vertically held rod. Alternatively, H can be determined by means of a stadia conversion table (Anderson, 1937) or, most simply, it can be read directly from the Beaman horizontal correction scale that is found on most telescopic alidades.

The difference in elevation between the instrument station and the base of the stadia rod comprises three factors: (1) *H.I.*, the height of the instrument above the instrument station, (2) the vertical distance between the instrument and the point on the rod that is read from the horizontal cross hair, and (3) the height of this point above the base of the rod (*R.C.*, rod correction). The *H.I.* is easily measured with a tape or with the stadia rod for each plane-table set up. The vertical distance, V, between the instrument and the rod reading can be calculated from the vertical angle a and the rod intercept AB as corrected to AC (see Fig. 3–25) according to the formula $V = S \sin a = AB \cos a \sin a\, 100 = AB\, (½ \sin 2a)\, 100$. This distance also can be determined simply by means of the Beaman arc scale.

In Fig. 3–25, the difference in elevation between the instrument station and the base of the stadia rod is $H.I. + V - DE$. Here DE is the rod correction (*R.C.*), and is usually read on the horizontal cross hair of the alidade. In brushy country, it may not be possible to see the intersection of the rod and the horizontal cross hair; the rod reading then may be made on the upper or on the lower stadia hair, and that reading corrected by subtracting or adding, respectively, one half of the rod intercept.

PLANE TABLE AND TELESCOPIC ALIDADE

The reading of vertical angles and the subsequent calculation of distances and elevations can be eliminated if the alidade is equipped with a Beaman stadia arc or a gradienter drum. The Beaman arc comprises two graduated arcs on, or attached to, the vertical-angle arc of the instrument. The vertical Beaman arc (VERT.) reads 50 when the telescope is level, and the entire scale is graduated from 10 to 90. These divisions are spaced so that as the telescope is raised or lowered, the arc scale shows the vertical difference, expressed in stadia intervals, between the instrument and the point on the rod corresponding to the horizontal cross hair. Points of higher elevation give readings greater than 50, whereas rod points lower than the alidade read less than 50 on the scale.

The vertical correction is the number of scale divisions greater or less than 50; it is multiplied by the rod intercept to give the elevation difference between the instrument and rod reading. For example, if the Beaman vertical reading is 61 and the *R.I.* is 3.84, the corrected vertical height is $+ 11 \times 3.84$, which equals $+ 42.24$ feet. This height is the V of Fig. 3–25.

The horizontal (HOR.) distance scale of the Beaman arc is either of two types. On one type, the scale reads downward from 100 percent, whereas on the other, the scale reads from zero upward. The first kind of scale gives a percentage of correction for converting slope or stadia distance. For example, if the *R.I.* is 3.84 and the horizontal scale reads 98.8, the corrected horizontal distance is 98.8 percent of 384 feet, or 379 feet. On the second type of scale, the horizontal reading for the same station would be 1.2; this multiplied by 384 is 5 feet for the correction. Subtracting 5 from 384 gives 379 feet, the horizontal distance. Thus the horizontal scale eliminates the need for trigonomertic corrections or stadia tables in determining horizontal distance.

A typical instrument man's notebook page, reflecting use of the Beaman method, is illustrated on Fig. 3–26. Note that the *R.C.*, rod correction, is always algebraically negative, being subtracted from the vertical correction on shots to higher points and added to the negative vertical correction on shots to points lower than the instrument's elevation.

The gradienter drum is used chiefly on long-range shots more applicable to topographic surveying than section measurements. The gradienter is a cylinder so calibrated into 100 divisions that one complete revolution moves the telescopic line of sight of the alidade upward or downward through exactly one stadia interval. In typical use of this device, the horizontal cross hair is lined in with the lowest visible full-foot mark of the stadia rod, the gradienter reading recorded, then the

DATE June 5, 19 52   GEOL. Kottlowski   INSTR. Bundy   PAGE 11
SECTION Northern Oscura Mts.   LOCATION NE¼ SE¼ Sec.36, T. 5 S, R. 5 E.

INSTR. STA.	ROD STA.	R.I.	R.C.	BEAMAN V	BEAMAN H	VERT. CORR.	HOR. DIST.	DIFF. ELEV.	ELEV. INSTR.	H.I.	ELEV.	REMARKS
17	18	6.15	-7.1	56	99.4	+36.9	611	+29.8	6159.1	3.7	6188.9	El.17 = 6155.4
18	17	6.15	-6.1	45	99.5	-30.8	611	-36.9	6192.5	3.6	6155.6	#18 base NOM 27
18	19	0.92	-0.6	51	99.9	+0.9	92	+0.3	–	–	6192.8	base NOM 28
–	20	1.35	-2.8	53	99.7	+4.1	135	+1.3	–	–	6193.8	base NOM 29
–	21	1.97	-4.1	57	99.3	+13.8	196	+9.7	–	–	6202.2	base NOM 30
–	22	2.74	-5.9	62	98.5	+32.9	270	+27.0	–	–	6219.5	base NOM 31

Fig. 3–26. Instrument notes for Beaman method of planetable section measurement.

PLANE TABLE AND TELESCOPIC ALIDADE

drum's tangent screw is turned to elevate the telescope until the same cross hair is on the highest visible full-foot mark, and that gradienter reading is recorded. The difference between the two cross-hair readings is divided by the difference between the two gradienter readings and multiplied by 100 to obtain the stadia distance. For example, if the first cross-hair reading is on the 3-foot mark with a gradienter reading of 0.32, and the second reading on the 12-foot mark is 0.76, the stadia distance would be 9 divided by 0.44 multiplied by 100 equaling 2045 feet.

Differences in elevation are calculated from the level line of sight. Assuming the stadia interval to be 20.45, as just determined, the telescope is leveled. If the rod point is above the level line, the horizontal cross hair is brought from level up to the base of the stadia rod. With a difference in readings of 0.32 on the gradienter, for example, the difference in elevation between the alidade and the rod base is 0.32 × 20.45 equaling 6.54 feet. If the rod point is below the level line, the horizontal cross hair is set on the top of the rod, and the telescope is then brought up to level; if, for example, the difference in the readings on the gradienter is 0.41, the difference in elevation between the alidade and the top of the stadia rod would be 0.41 × 20.45 equaling 8.38 feet. If the rod is 13 feet long, the vertical difference to the base of the rod would be 21.38 feet.

The telescopic alidade is a precision instrument; it must be handled with care, should be constantly checked, and adjustments made in the field if possible (see Low, 1952, and others for details). As at least two persons are required and three workers desirable, section measuring by plane-tabling, although accurate, can be costly because it consumes a relatively high number of man hours. The method is most applicable in areas of low to moderate relief where the beds dip at low to moderate angles and form wide outcrop bands, and where precise measurements of distance and elevation are necessary to determine the exact thicknesses of the measured units.

In rugged areas of high relief, the plane-tabling equipment is relatively difficult to move and set up, and correct determination of vertical angles and horizontal distances requires slow, careful readings and calculations. An objectionably large number of instrument stations may be necessary in order to sight the various measured units.

If some of the measured units, in areas of moderate relief, are thinner than 5 or 6 feet, their thicknesses should be determined by some other method, such as the stadia rod used as a Jacob staff with a Brunton compass employed as the clinometer. Unless one is working in areas of low relief where the rock units dip gently and form extremely wide outcrop bands, any of the other applicable techniques for establishing control can be used effectively—direct measurement with short tape, Jacob staff, and hand level, or thicknesses calculated from measurements with the Brunton compass, Abney hand level, and the like. Stadia rod points then can be set chiefly on the boundaries of major lithologic units or spaced adequately throughout the section in order to minimize cumulative errors.

The plane-tabling party for measuring stratigraphic sections ideally consists of three persons, a geologist, his assistant, and an instrument man. The instrument man "runs" the telescopic alidade and plots the location and elevation of each point in the measured-section traverse on the plane-table sheet. His field notes, if the Beaman method is used, normally are like those shown on Fig. 3–26. Unless a complete geologic and topographic map is made along with the measuring of the section, the plot is merely a framework of sight lines, instrument points, and rod points (Fig. 3–27). Approximate boundaries of units along the line of section may be sketched on the plane-table sheet by the instrument man.

The geologist and his assistant share the placing of the stadia rod, determination of strikes and dips, description of the lithologic units, collection of rock samples and fossils, and painting or otherwise labeling

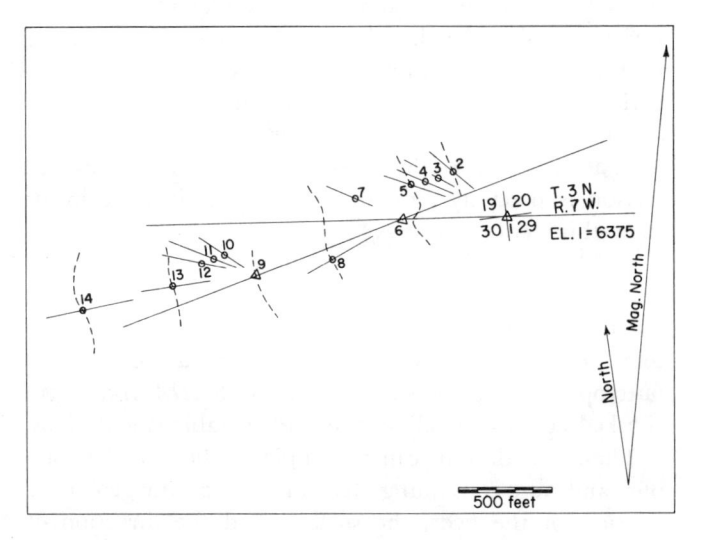

Fig. 3–27. Plane-table plot of measured section.

of the units if this is considered necessary. They are also responsible for interpolative measuring of units between rod points. Ordinarily, the geologist directs the placing of unit boundaries, describes the lithology of the units, and indicates rock samples and fossils to be collected; he also may measure strikes, dips, and the thickness of supplementary units. The assistant holds the stadia rod on rod points, measures strikes and dips, paints the unit boundaries and numbers on the outcrop, and collects the indicated rock samples and fossils.

Typical field notes, made while measuring the units plotted on the plane-table map of Fig. 3-27, are shown in Fig. 3-28. This section was measured in gently dipping Upper Cretaceous beds, with rod points 2 to 5 on the ledgy face of a cuesta, and the remainder of the section was traced down a dip slope to the west. The starting point, instrument station 1, was a section corner; its elevation was carried in from a bench mark with a Paulin altimeter. However, any arbitrarily chosen elevation, such as 1000 feet, could be used as a base. The measured section is precisely located in a geographic sense by its tie to this section corner.

Thicknesses of units not measured directly in the field (for example, $Ak1$, $Ak2$, $Ak6$) were calculated from the plane-table data after the day's field work, and the total thicknesses of some thin units measured on the outcrop with a Jacob staff (such as, $Ak3$, $Ak4$, $Ak5$) were checked against the alidade and plane-table calculations.

These calculations can be simple or they can be complex and time consuming, depending upon the geometric relation of the beds, the surface, and the direction of traverse. For example, the thickness of unit $Ak1$ was determined by measurements to rod points R2 and R3. The direction of traverse from R2 to R3 is S. 81° W. whereas the direction of dip is S. 83° W. The correction for the angle of variance for a traverse measured oblique to the dip is given by the formula: the distance normal to the strike equals oblique distance measured times the cosine of the angle between the two lines. In this case, the angle is merely 2°, its cosine 0.999; thus no correction is necessary.

Knowing the difference in elevation V, the angle of

SECTION Alamo Day School
LOCATION secs. 19 & 30, T. 3 N, R. 7 W.
COUNTY Socorro, N. Mex.
FORMATIONS La Cruz Peak
BY F. Kott & Larry Herber
DATE 6/19/62

UNIT NO.	FEET	ROCK TYPE	SURVEY NOTES, ROCK COLOR, GRAINS, CEMENT, BEDS, STRUCTURES, WNG., TOPO, FOSSILS
—	-	—	∆1 at sect cor 19-20-30-29, T.3N,R.7W. Paulin El.6375
Ak1-b	-	Ss	R2, base ledgy cliff; med. grd.; well-sort; quartz; silica-cement; bds 2-12'; mas.; wn yel.-brn., Fe-stained; St. N.9°W., Dip 12°SW; RS Ak1a, 10' above base. l.gy - gy.
Ak1-t	106	"	R3, top ledge of Ak1; RS Ak1b in middle; RS Ak1c 5' from top
Ak2	48	Sh,car.	Blk; minor silt; clayey to fissile; slope; lam bone coal nr top; top of Ak1: St.N.14°W., Dip 12°SW. RS AK2 fr top
Ak3-b	6	Ss	R4, base ledges; gy; med-grd; well-sort; quartz; silica cem.; beds 3-12", friable ledges; petrified wood frags. RS Ak3 fr. top
Ak4	7	Ss	p.gn.to p.red; fn-grd; quartz; silica-cem; bds 1-2', hard ledges; St. N.10°W., Dip 11°SW; RS Ak4 fr. middle.
Ak5-t	6	Ss	R5 at top; gy. med-grd; well-sort; mod. consol; ± friable; quartz; silica - cem.; mas., unbdd.; rdd yel-brn. ledge; RS Ak5 at top. (thkness Ak3-Ak5 chkd = 19')
—	-	—	∆6 on crest of cuesta; dip slope on Ak5
Ak6-t	11	Sh	R7; gy; clayey to fissile; partly cov; slope; sty lam.

Fig. 3–28. Rodman's (geologist's) field notes made while measuring a section with plane table and telescopic alidade.

dip a, and horizontal distance perpendicular to the strike H, the stratigraphic thickness T is found from the formula (Fig. 3–29) $T = H \sin a + V \cos a$. Here the dip angle is 12°, H measured from the plot is 87 feet, and V calculated from the alidade shot is 90 feet; substituting, we find that $T = 87 \sin 12° + 90 \cos 12°$; therefore T is 106 feet.

In this and many other situations, the two rod points (that is, $R2$ and $R3$) are so close together that the horizontal distance between them cannot be accurately scaled from the plane-table map. The horizontal distances from instrument station 1 to the two rod points are determined by alidade calculations (*R.I.* times horizontal Beaman correction), the angle f between the two lines of sight is measured from the plane-table plot, and the horizontal distance between the two rod points is then calculated

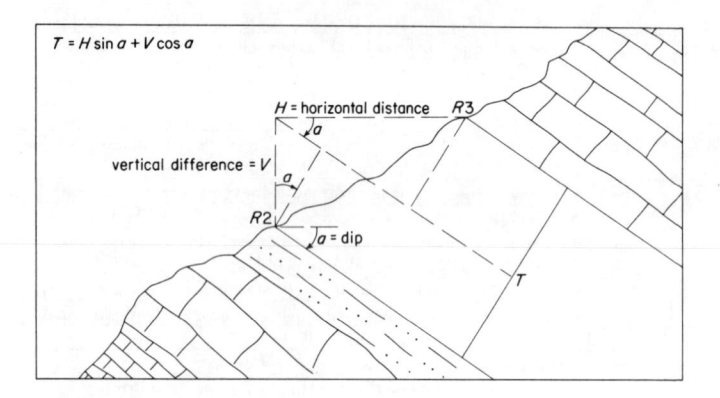

Fig. 3–29. Sketch for determining thickness from plane table and alidade data for a section measured normal to the strike of layers.

from the trigonometric formula: $A^2 = B^2 + C^2 - 2BC \cos f$, where B and C are the known horizontal distances and f is the angle between their lines of sight.

In this example, B, the horizontal distance from point 1 to $R2$, is 362 feet; C, the horizontal distance from point 1 to $R3$, is 416 feet; and angle f is $10°$. Therefore A, the horizontal distance $R2$ to $R3$, is equal to the square root of $[(362)^2 + (416)^2 - 2 \times 362 \times 416 \cos 10°]$. It can be pointed out that plane-table and alidade measurements commonly involve considerable trigonometric computations when they are used for controlling measured sections.

TRANSIT AND TAPE MEASUREMENTS

A transit can be likened to an alidade that is mounted on a horizontal arc instead of on a base plate with a fiducial edge. The major difference is that, since the transit is not mounted on a plane-table map board, the field data cannot be plotted as they are obtained. Instead, they are recorded in a notebook, and plotting is usually done later in an office where drafting boards are available. Alternatively, the plotting can be done in the field on a separate map board, but this is a process independent of the transit itself. The transit does have the advantage of providing a greater vertical range than an alidade.

The transit and tape method is used when greater accuracy is desired than can be obtained from ordinary plane-table surveying. Vertical angles can be measured more precisely with a transit than with a telescopic alidade if the transit vertical-angle arc is graduated to the nearest 20 minutes of arc. The general procedure in obtaining vertical angles is the same for both instruments. Distances to intermediate rod shots for important points along the measured section can be determined by stadia, but distances and differences in elevation between instrument stations should be surveyed, for precision, by reading vertical angles and taping the distances directly on the outcrop surface.

The transit and tape technique is most applicable where the country is too rugged and slopes too steep for an efficient plane-table traverse, and where a precise, staked traverse line is desired. Considering that the readings recorded must be plotted in a separate operation and the bearings from one point to another determined by vertical angle readings, use of the transit is a much slower procedure than that with a plane table and alidade.

Taping is a precise and relatively swift method of determining level and slope distances, except in extremely rugged cliffy terrain. It is applicable in most rough, brushy, or heavily forested mountainous country where some other methods of measurement, particularly the plane table and alidade technique, are difficult to employ. Cloth tapes, metal-woven cloth tapes, and steel tapes in lengths of 25, 50, or 100 feet are available, and each has its advantages. A 100-foot steel tape, however, is recommended as the most satisfactory type for measuring sections, because it is long enough for measurements across thick units and it is strong enough to take the constant wear and tear of contact with sharp edges on rock outcrops.

TRANSIT AND TAPE MEASUREMENTS

A careful traverse in which distances are obtained by taping will yield the most accurate measurements of any type of survey. For this reason, base lines set up as the major control for a mapping project or for highly precise measurements of a stratigraphic section are commonly laid out with a tape. The taping procedure may be adapted, of course, to give various degrees of accuracy. In general it is most rapid and precise if the distances can be measured across a nearly level surface, with the tape held level to give exact measurement of horizontal distance. Compton (1962) has noted that such measurements need not be in error by more than one part in 2000. Such accuracy rarely is necessary in section measuring.

In general surveying it is often possible to select a course along which the tape can be held level, but this rarely is the case in measuring sections, where the traverse ordinarily is made across outcrops on a slope. Two men are required, and it is helpful to have some taping pins to mark points of measurement. In transit and tape work, the instrument man holds the 100-foot mark or some other mark of the tape directly on the point beneath the transit, or on a stake set on the transit ground point, using a plumb bob hung from the transit if such accuracy is desired. The lead tapeman carries the zero end of the tape to the measured point, both men hold the tape with about a ten-pound pull, and the lead man marks the point with a taping pin or marks directly on the outcrop with a colored "paint pencil."

If the distance is less than 100 feet, it is appropriately recorded. If it is more than 100 feet, the instrument man then becomes the "rear" tapeman, moving to the point just marked by the lead tapeman as the lead tapeman moves forward and establishes another point for measuring. This process is repeated as necessary.

On a level surface, the taped distance is the horizontal distance; however, on a slope the vertical angle of the taped line must be determined in order to obtain the horizontal distance. Where the vertical angle is 6° or more, it should be determined by means of a transit shot to a point at instrument height above the final measured point. The instrument height can be sighted on a stadia rod held at the measured point, or on an indicated spot on the steel tape held vertically over the point by the lead tapeman.

When the vertical angle is less than 6°, a horizontal distance correction is too small to be significant, and the vertical angle can be read by sighting from the transit to the ground point or taping pin.

BRUNTON COMPASS AND TAPE MEASUREMENTS

The Brunton compass and tape method is usually satisfactory for measuring sections where the layers dip more than 10° and intersect the surface at a fairly large angle. By fastening one end of the tape on the outcrop (as to a stake, bush, or rock projection), one geologist can make the measurements, but they are less accurate and more difficult to double-check than those made by a two-man team. As noted earlier in the discussion of tape and transit techniques, the main difficulty is that steep vertical angles should be sighted along a line parallel to the tape, and not from a standing position at one point to the ground at the second point.

BRUNTON COMPASS AND TAPE MEASUREMENTS

Each unit can be measured separately, especially if the units are thick and crop out on slopes that are uniform within each unit. If the units are thin and can be measured over fairly long composite slopes, the tape can be stretched from one break in slope to the next, and the units within each of the taped distances marked. The following procedure, modified from that suggested by Compton (1962), can be employed:

1. The lead tapeman carries the tape from the base of the section to be measured to the first break in the slope; preferably this break is also a boundary between two measured units. The rear tapeman retains the zero end of the tape and secures it to the outcrop, usually by tying it to a stake, while the lead tapeman is fastening the tape at the break in the slope; this may be the 100-foot end of the tape or any intermediate point along the tape.
2. Both observers read their Brunton compasses to obtain (a) the bearing of the taped line, and (b) the slope angle. The slope angle, especially when it is relatively large, should be read along a line of sight parallel to the tape; if both observers are about the same height, they should sight at each other's eyes when reading the slope angle (Fig. 3–30). When the two-man team is a Mutt-and-Jeff combination of a short and a tall man, the short person sights low and the tall person high; the angles should check closely.
3. With the tape stretched along the slope of the outcrops, the rocks are described and the boundaries of units recorded by slope-distance measurements read directly from the tape. Contacts between units may require projection along their dip to the tape for correct reading of the slope distance (Fig. 3–31). The measurements are recorded and the units described from the base of the section by the rear

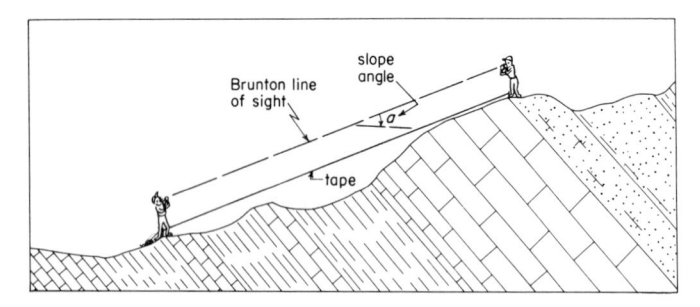

Fig. 3–30. Sighting slope angle for Brunton and tape traverse.

tapeman. Meanwhile, the lead tapeman determines and records strikes and dips of the layers, collects rock samples and fossils, and labels the units with a paint-pencil if this is desirable.

These three steps are repeated as the section is progressively measured. If the units are measured individually, the lead tapeman may carry the zero end of the tape and the slope distance is then read by the rear

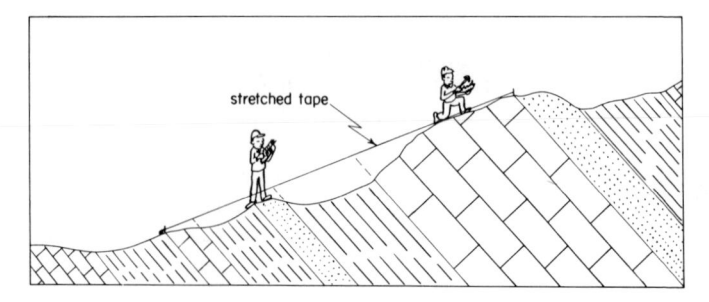

Fig. 3–31. Measuring thickness of units from a stretched tape, projecting contacts to the tape along the apparent dip.

tapeman; this method eliminates the need for fastening the tape to the outcrops by stakes. In many areas of good exposures, it is difficult to find either a spot where a stake can be driven or some natural object to which the tape can be secured.

Fig. 3–32 illustrates field notes of a section measured by Brunton compass and tape in the Beartooth Mountains of south-central Montana. The rocks are part of the

SECTION Rock Creek, Beartooth Mts. FORMATIONS Bighorn Dol.
LOCATION SE¼ NW¼ sec. 17, T.8 S., R.20 W. BY F. Kott & R. Horton
COUNTY Carbon, Montana DATE 7/14/47

UNIT NO.	CAL. FEET	ROCK TYPE	BEARING, TAPED DIST., SLOPE, ST. and DIP; COLOR, GRAINS, CEMENT, BEDS, STRUCTURES, WNG., TOPO., FOSSILS
RC1	4	Dol	Meas. direct; p.yel. to pk-gy., fn-xl, mas; wrs. gy. rough; base of ledgy cliffs; RS 4701–1½' above base.
RC2	14	Dol	B.N. 59°E., +22', +16°; St.N.35°W., Dip 56°W.(all over turned); p.yel., fn-xl, mas bds 6-8'; some breccia zone recemented by wh xl calc; wrs. buff, rough; ledgy cliffs; R.S. 4702 nr top.
RC3	31	Dol	B.N. 70°E., +43',+11°; St N.37°W., Dip 60°W.; p.yel; fn- to med-xl, bds 1-2' thk; wrs l.gy, ledgy cliffs; scat sil nod nr top; RS 4703 of same sil nod and dol.
RC4	37	Dol	B.N. 61°E., +43',+2°; St.N.36°W., Dip 62°W.; tan, med-grd, sugary, porous; mas wi faint 2' bdng planes; fetid; buff, rough, mas. ledges; RS 4704 nr center
RC5	23	Dol	B.N 72°E., +24',-31°; St.N.37°W., Dip 60°W.; lith as RC4 but scat. sil nod.; RS 4705 in upper 5'
RC6	28	Dol	B.N. 33°E., +30',-44°; St.N.34°W., Dip 53°W.; p.yel, fn-xl, mas bds 3'; wrs. gy, smooth, cliffy; many irreg sil nod ave 2" dia, range to 8"; sil horn corals; F.S. 4704 nr. top; RS 4706 8' above base
RC7	69	Dol	B.N. 39°E., +80½',-15°; St.N.30°W., Dip 50°W.; l.gy mottled l. brn, crs-xl; mas with few l' bds nr base; wrs tan, pitted; ocs ledgy cliff; RS 4707 12' below top

Fig. 3–32. Typical field notes for a stratigraphic section measured by Brunton compass and tape.

Paleozoic section exposed on the northeast margin of the range, where the beds are overturned and crop out as steeply dipping palisades with intervening ledgy slopes. Items noted in the field include: (1) bearing of the tape line, (2) taped slope distance, (3) slope angle, (4) strike and dip, and (5) lithologic features of the rocks. The stratigraphic thickness is calculated by the following steps, with S the slope distance measured on the tape, a the slope angle, and d the angle of dip.

1. Determine the divergence angle c of the taped-line direction from the dip direction by finding the angle between tape bearing and a bearing normal to the strike. If the strike is N. 46° W. and the bearing of the tape N. 62° E., the direction of west dip is along a S. 44° W. (N. 44° E.) line; therefore the divergence angle c is 18°.
2. P, the perpendicular distance along the dip direction, is estimated from the simple formula $P = S \cos c$ (Fig. 3–33). This formula yields results accurate to within one degree if both angles a and c are 20° or less—the situation for most sections measured. The taped slope distance S in the example is 43 feet; therefore $P = 43 \cos 18° = 41$ feet.
3. The perpendicular slope angle b is found by the formula $\tan b = \tan a / \cos c$. The slope angle measured in the example is + 17°; substituting, we find that $\tan b = \tan 17° / \cos 18°$; $\tan d = 0.321$; b is 18°.
4. The apparent or combined angle of the stratigraphic thickness e is equal to the perpendicular slope angle b plus or minus the angle of dip d. For measurements downhill, if the bearing of the taped line is in the direction opposite the dip, add d; if the bearing is in the same direction as the dip, subtract d. For measurements uphill, subtract d if the bearing of the taped line is in the direction opposite the dip, and add d if the bearing is in the same direction as the dip. In the example, the bearing is in the direction

opposite the dip direction and the distance was taped uphill; thus d is subtracted from b; as d is 62° W., e is 44° (−44°).

5. The stratigraphic thickness T is then given by $T = P \sin e$; $T = 41 \sin 44°$; $T = 28$ feet.

Relations showing correction of slope distance S to perpendicular distance P using the divergence angle c are shown in Fig. 3–33. If the slope angle of divergence c' is used, $P = S \cos c'$; when angle c, the actual divergence angle, and a are less than 20°, angle c' is within one degree of angle c. As readings with a compass commonly are within only one degree accuracy, and most sections are measured across outcrops where angles a and c are less than 20°, the foregoing formula is quick and simple to use. Angle c, of course, is the divergence angle measured in the field; its relation to angle c' is

$\sin c' = \sin c \cos a$ $P = S \cos c'$

slope angle of divergence

strike and dip

perpendicular slope distance P

oblique slope distance S

slope angle

actual angle of divergence

perpendicular slope angle

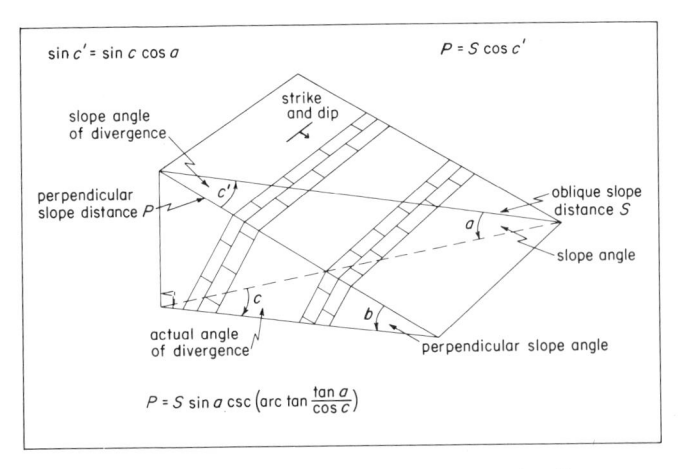

$P = S \sin a \csc \left(\arctan \dfrac{\tan a}{\cos c} \right)$

Fig. 3–33. Correction of taped slope distance for divergence from direction of dip.

shown by the formula $\sin c' = \sin c \cos a$, indicating that c is never smaller than c'. To obtain the the perpendicular slope distance from the dimensions measured, S, a, and c, one formula is $P = S \sin a \csc [\arc \tan (\tan a / \cos c)]$!

The correction of the slope angle a to the perpendicular slope angle b (the slope angle in the vertical plane perpendicular to the strike) similarly is derived from trigonometric relations. Calculation of the apparent angle e (also known as the combined angle) of the stratigraphic thickness depends on the relative positions of the dip and the direction of slope; the four general cases are described in Chapter 4 (Figs. 4–8 to 4–13).

This method of calculating the stratigraphic thicknesses from Brunton compass and tape measurements may seem cumbersome, but it is a logical step-by-step procedure that allows checks on the magnitude of the corrections as each step is calculated.

The thicknesses can be computed from the single formula derived by Mertie (1922) and illustrated by Billings (1954). Use of this formula may save some time but it involves almost as much trigonometric manipulation. The formula is $T = S (\sin d \cos a \sin z \pm \sin a \cos d)$ where z is the azimuth of the traverse, the horizontal angle between the strike of the beds and the direction in which the slope distance is measured; d is the dip angle and a the slope angle. The two products are added together if the dip of the beds and the slope of the ground are in opposite directions; if the dip and slope are in the same direction, the second product is subtracted from the first.

The Brunton and tape method of section measuring is sufficiently accurate for most purposes, and it is applicable over most types of surface relief and for layers dipping at angles of 10° or more, especially if the layered rocks intersect the surface at relatively high angles, say 20° or more. The angle of divergence, c, between the direction of dip and the line of measurement, should be kept as small as possible. Except for measuring down steep cliffs, the tape can be held correctly at almost any slope angle, but in actual practice slope angles of more than 40° are difficult to read and errors may well be greater than the 1° limit of precision of Brunton-angle readings.

If the plane of the beds is at right angles to the ground surface, the thicknesses can be measured directly by running the traverse perpendicular to the strike and dip. The Brunton and tape technique is much faster than that of plane-tabling, and with practice can be almost as rapid as that involving use of the Jacob staff. In addition, it can be employed across beds that dip too steeply for Jacob staff work. One of its chief disadvantages, shared with plane-tabling, is the amount of mathematical calculation involved. Use of a slide rule shortens the time necessary to make calculations, but the rule must be handled carefully to avoid errors. However, if the traverse is run normal to the strike of the layers, a simplified circular slide rule, such as the "strati-rule" prepared by Threet (1961), may be used.

BRUNTON COMPASS AND PACE MEASUREMENTS

Rapid reconnaissance measurements can be made with a compass and pace traverse, especially in areas of low relief. The method is that used in normal compass-pace surveys for geologic mapping, in which directions and slope angles are determined with the Brunton compass and distances are measured by pacing. The steeper the dip of the layers to be measured, especially where dips are greater than 20°, the less satisfactory this method becomes, as errors in control are translated into increasing errors in computed thickness of units. However, the measurements can be made quickly by one person and sections composed of thick uniform lithic units can be measured in this manner with reasonable precision.

Combinations of this with other techniques often are desirable. In those parts of a section where thin units crop out along a level surface or on a low, even slope, for example, measurements can be made with a tape or by using a Jacob staff. In high cuts along a road or stream, thicknesses can be taped directly on the rocks, or measured with a Jacob staff. Where thicker units cover a broad outcrop band, the Brunton and pace method can be utilized effectively.

Pacing is one of the oldest methods of measuring distance, and yields accurate results if done with care. The geologist merely counts the number of his steps while walking between points, and then multiplies the total by the average length of his pace. To find his average pace, he walks a measured course of several thousand feet and counts the number of paces, then divides the distance by the total number of paces. He may count each step, or count each time either his left foot or his right foot hits the ground. A natural, uniform stride should be consciously cultivated until it becomes automatic. Most geologists calibrate variations in their pace lengths for level, uphill, and downhill travel in order to achieve consistency in horizontal distance; others automatically compensate the length of their steps on slopes so that the horizontal equivalents of their paces remain uniform.

The chief source of error in pacing is miscounting the number of steps taken; thus a tally counter or a pedometer should be used for counting to avoid mental miscalculations. The tally counter is a small watch-sized register on which a knob is pressed for each count; the accumulative number is displayed automatically. As it operates only when pressed, the geologist may stop and examine outcrops or may make offsets in his line of traverse, and then resume the count along the same line or along a parallel line of sight. A pedometer tallies automatically for each step, therefore its count must be corrected for broken paces and interruptions in the measured line of traverse.

The line of measured section should be paced, whenever possible, normal to the strike of the rock units. Data noted in the field notebook are: (1) bearing of the traverse, (2) slope angle (if any), (3) strikes and dips of layers, (4) paced distance, and (5) lithologic descriptions of the units. Both the readings and mathematical calculations are similar to those used in the Brunton and tape method; with either method, it is also convenient to draw a sketch map in the notebook while the traverse is being made. Obvious errors then can be seen at a glance while the geologist is still in the field. This spares him from trying to find the errors later while calculating stratigraphic thicknesses. Too, he otherwise may overlook some errors altogether.

The traverse for the measured section should be "closed" back to the starting point whenever possible as a check on accuracy of control. The section can be measured, then a parallel or shorter route comprising longer traverse segments and fewer stations can be followed back to the initial point. The original section also can be checked by following it backward, point by point, to the starting station.

MEASUREMENTS FROM MAPS AND PHOTOGRAPHS

If an accurate, detailed geologic map is available for an area and if the lithologic units are uniform laterally, the thickness of each delineated unit can be calculated directly from the map, using its outcrop breadth perpendicular to the strike, the dip of the layers, and differences in elevation. Topographic maps and aerial photographs also can be used as bases on which contacts of lithic units are plotted. Thicknesses then can be calculated if distances are scaled off from the maps or photographs, dips are measured in the field or otherwise determined, and if elevations are derived from contours on the topographic maps, estimated photogrammetrically, or measured on the ground by altimeter or other methods.

This technique is most commonly used for checking total thickness of a section or part of a section that has been measured in more detail by other methods; for measuring thick, lithologically uniform units such as 200 feet of massive sandstone; for measuring thick, variable units such as 1200 feet of a volcanic sequence; and for reconnaissance checking of sections for possibly more detailed measurements.

Boundaries of lithic units can be located more easily, in

general, on an aerial photograph than on a topographic map, since they commonly appear on the photograph as linear changes in tone, pattern, and texture, or they lie near readily identifiable objects such as bushes, trees, trails, waterways, and anthills. However, once the features are properly located and plotted, measurements on topographic maps generally are more accurate, because many features on aerial photographs are displaced from their actual positions, owing to relief of the terrain, tilt of the airplane when the photograph was taken, or other factors. Elevations can be determined from topographic maps, but are obtainable from photographs only through special methods of stereoscopic projection.

Detailed sections cannot be measured by this method, and the thicknesses obtained may be in error by 10 percent or more. However, for some purposes of geologic mapping, control for structural studies and for compositional trends of sedimentation, rapid measurement of many sections is desirable; gross lithic units can be examined and compared over large areas by the technique of measuring on topographic maps and aerial photographs. Numerous sections of layered volcanic rocks, ranging for example from a megascopically uniform welded tuff hundreds of feet thick to a complex of thin, lenticular, intimately intertongued flows, tuffs, and volcanic sediments, can be measured on aerial photographs to determine some of their regional relations. Indeed, their thickness and lithology may be so variable that detailed measurements of sections are unnecessary.

Relations among the Upper Cretaceous strata of the San Juan Basin in northwestern New Mexico have been effectively determined by means of sections measured from aerial photographs and topographic maps. The sequence is dominated by alternating sandstones, sandy shales, dark marine shales, and some coal beds. Within a typical 15-minute quadrangle, a formation such as the Mancos Shale may contain four sandstone lenses in the southern part of the area and only one in the northern part. Measurement of many sections throughout such a quadrangle is necessary to reveal the pinch-outs and intertonguing relations.

Applying photogeologic methods of mapping, the geologist can quickly determine, in the office, those areas where critical exposures occur. A few detailed sections, perhaps evenly spaced throughout the map area, can be measured on the ground by means of the Jacob staff or other techniques. Supplementary sections then can be measured from the map in order to interpret the broad relationships of intertonguing and pinching-out among the sandstone and shale units.

Using a topographic map in the field, the geologist locates points on the contacts of lithic units along a line of outcrops about parallel to the dip direction, takes strikes and dips, describes the lithology, and collects samples and fossils as needed. Calculations of thickness are then similar to, but simpler than, those used for a Brunton and tape traverse; the bearing of the line of measurement and the horizontal distance are scaled from the map, and vertical differences in elevation of unit-boundary points are determined from the topographic contours. The angle of divergence between the line of section and the dip direction is calculated, and the horizontal distance is corrected by the formula $H = D \cos c$, where H is the corrected horizontal distance, D the horizontal distance measured on the map, and c the angle of divergence. If the difference in elevation of two unit boundaries is the same across the dip as along the line of the measured section, the stratigraphic thickness is calculated from the formula, $T = H \sin a + V \cos a$, where T is the stratigraphic thickness, a the angle of dip, and V the difference in elevation (Fig. 3–29).

If aerial photographs are used, the geologist also locates contacts of the lithic units in the field, plots them on the photograph, takes strikes and dips, and describes the rocks. The bearing of the line of measurement and the distance between points are scaled from the photographs, after the scale and cardinal directions are determined for the photographs and plotted thereon. The latter can be done by referring to a map of the area and scaling off the direction and distance between two points known both on the map and on the photograph. Differences in elevation must be found by supplementary means, for example, vertical angles determined with a Brunton compass or measurements with a Paulin altimeter. Calculations of stratigraphic thicknesses are then made as outlined in the previous paragraph.

ALTIMETER MEASUREMENTS

The Paulin altimeter is an accurate aneroid barometer with a scale that can be read to the nearest 2 feet, although the smallest graduations are in 10-foot units. The instrument is designed to measure the altitude of an occupied field point; if it is correctly set for atmospheric pressure and temperature, as by reference to a surveyed point occupied a short time earlier, it will record the elevation of a point above sea level. As the pressure and temperature can vary greatly with time, corrections must be made for pressure variations, both diurnal and those due to weather changes, and in many instruments for temperature changes as well.

All aneroids are delicate instruments that must be handled carefully and must not be jarred. They are not suitable for very precise work, their limit of accuracy being about 2 to 5 feet vertically. In unsettled weather, and especially under thunderstorm conditions, they are essentially useless. Checking back to a point of known altitude, such as a bench mark, at intervals of several hours or less is one way of correcting for barometric pressure variations. For the detailed corrections that are necessary, see Lahee (1961, pages 461–490), who noted that with careful work the average relative error can be less than one vertical in 1000 horizontal.

The altimeter can be used for determining elevations of points located on aerial photographs, and for interpolation between contours or for locating points on topographic maps. It is especially useful in brushy or forested country where open views of the terrain are limited, and for measuring sections in areas where the strata dip at such low angles they form wide outcrop bands not well suited to measurements with a Jacob staff or Brunton compass. The Paulin altimeter is a reconnaissance tool that in general is not satisfactory for measuring detailed sections, but it is more useful for work with thick uniform units in situations where differences of elevation need not be determined with a high degree of accuracy. Ordinarily, the altimeter is employed

ALTIMETER MEASUREMENTS

to determine elevations of contact points between lithic units of a measured section, with the horizontal distance (or slope distance) between the points obtained by means of pacing, or through scaling the located points from an aerial photograph or topographic map.

Items normally recorded in the field notebook when measuring a section employing a Paulin altimeter and Brunton compass are:

1. time of altimeter reading
2. elevation at base of unit
3. compass bearing to next occupied point at top of unit
4. paced distance to this next point
5. strike and dip of the layers
6. lithologic description of unit
7. rocks and fossils collected

When the altimeter points are plotted directly in the field on a photograph or topographic map, the bearings and paced distances are not needed.

Points also can be located horizontally by means of a Paulin altimeter and a topographic map. If a stratigraphic section is measured along one or more linear features that can be identified on the map (such as a stream channel, ridge, trail, or road), the elevation of a contact point between lithic units is read from the altimeter; then the point can be plotted on the map by reference to the contours. This approach not only determines differences in elevation between contact points, but also yields horizontal map distances.

In actual practice, the altimeter point should be plotted in the field on the topographic map. When the elevation reading is checked for accuracy and any necessary pressure and temperature corrections are made, it is plotted at the appropriate position on the topographic map. Calculations of stratigraphic thickness between points then are based upon differences in elevation, map distances, and bearings taken from the map. Data on strikes and dips also are necessary, and in most cases are measured with a Brunton compass. The topographic map should have a reasonably small contour interval, such as 20 feet, and should be on a scale of 1:24,000 or larger.

Points for a section in west-dipping beds, as measured with a Paulin altimeter, are shown on Fig. 3–34. This section was measured up a stream bed, offset southward to a trail, thence shifted to the head of a gully, and from there onto the edge of a cuesta peak, and was completed down a stream bed on the dip slope. The Paulin elevations at the bases of the first two units, *U*1 and *U*2, did

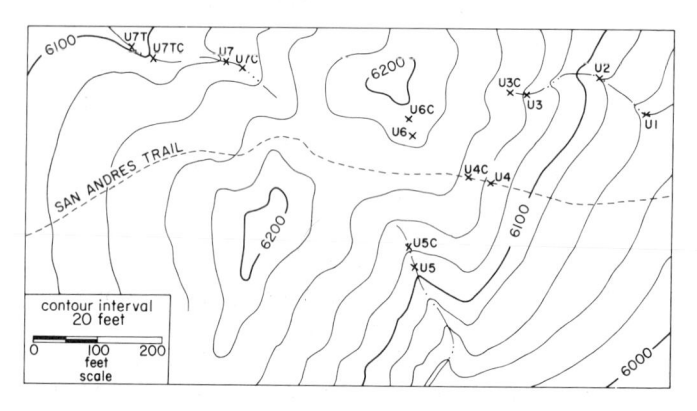

Fig. 3–34. Points on section measured with Paulin altimeter as plotted on a topographic map.

not need correction, but those for the other points were corrected to higher values and the points labeled *U3C* (Unit 3 corrected), *U4C,* and so on. The top of the highest lithic unit of the section is labeled *U7T* (Unit 7 top), with the corrected point being *U7TC*. Note that the plotted positions of the points were shifted in accord with the vertical corrections.

RAPID ESTIMATES BY PACE AND DIP

Rapid field estimation of thickness of lithologic units is sometimes needed. If the layers crop out on a gentle slope or level surface, and if their dip does not exceed 35°, the following rule applies (Geikie, 1920, page 301): If the width of inclined layers is measured by pacing across their outcrop in a direction at right angles to their strike, their true thickness will be equal to one twelfth of their apparent thickness for every 5° of dip. Or, stated differently, divide the dip by 60 to obtain the fraction that expresses the true thickness. As an example, if an exposed sequence of layers measures 1800 feet perpendicular to the strike, and if the layers dip 5°, the true thickness of the sequence is one twelfth of 1800 feet, or 150 feet. If the dip were 20°, the apparent thickness of 1800 feet would be divided by four twelfths or one third, and the true thickness would be 600 feet.

This rule is based on the sine of the dip angle. If the dip angle is *d,* and the apparent thickness measured in a horizontal plane and perpendicular to the strike is *A,* the true (stratigraphic) thickness, *T,* is equal to *A* sin *d*. Estimates by the method just outlined are essentially correct for dips of 30° or less, and would involve errors of less than one percent for dips of 30° to 35°. The result is 2.4 percent low for a dip of 40°, 4.3 percent low for 45°, and nearly 14 percent low for a dip of 60°. Within the limit of errors that can be expected in pacing, this rapid method of calculation is valid for estimating thicknesses of units that dip at angles of 40° or less.

COMBINATIONS OF CONTROL TECHNIQUES

Combinations of techniques often can be employed to measure a section quickly and accurately. No geologist should be wedded to one technique in a situation where it may be more desirable to use two or more. Direct scaling with a ruler, for example, should be done whenever practicable, and thin units often can be measured in this manner no matter what method is used for over-all control.

As noted by Low (1957, page 306), some of the most effective combinations involve use of the plane table for primary control. Rod points are located on prominent layers and unit boundaries; thicknesses of lithologic units between these rod points can be determined with a hand level, Jacob staff, or Brunton compass, or they can be measured directly on the edges of thin beds (Fig. 3–35). This approach provides the advantage of a double check on thicknesses and permits the tracing of key beds around topographic projections into areas of better exposures that are beyond the sight of the alidade. Close spacing of rod shots is not necessary,

COMBINATIONS OF CONTROL TECHNIQUES 131

leading to attendant reduction in mathematical calculations.

Measurements with the Brunton compass and steel tape can be conveniently combined with the Brunton compass eye-height technique, or with the Hewett method for thin units that dip at angles of less than 60° and can be measured along lines of traverse at right angles

Fig. 3–35. Traverse of section combining plane-tabling with other methods, the units between rod shots being measured with Hewett method, Jacob staff, or taped directly.

to the strike. The Jacob staff also can be employed with the compass-tape method, but this necessitates carrying an extra instrument, the staff. The advantage of direct measurements with the Jacob staff, offset by the extra chore of carrying the staff, must be balanced against the single calculation that transforms a Hewett-method thickness reading into stratigraphic thickness.

Most of the methods that involve accumulative types of measuring, such as those with the Jacob staff, eye-height techniques, compass and tape, and compass and pace, should be checked to avoid gross errors in total thickness or thicknesses of major parts of the section. An altimeter traverse, including only major points of the section, is one approach to rapidly verifying total thickness, especially if made in conjunction with a topographic map. A rapid traverse with plane table and alidade, or with transit and tape, provides a more accurate check; however, if it is used merely as such verification, the geologist should ask whether this traverse, perhaps in slightly greater detail, might have served effectively for primary control of the section.

Aerial photographs and topographic maps, when available, provide bases for quick and easy checking of thicknesses. The base and top points of the measured section are plotted on the photograph or map, the average strike and dip along the line between these two points is estimated, and the total thickness of section is calculated from the distance and bearing (scaled from the base) and the difference in elevation of the points. Elevation differences can be read from a topographic map, but in general they must be determined by some other means (for example, the Paulin altimeter) if aerial photographs are used.

In general, elevations and distances for the calculation of section thicknesses are most accurately measured by means of the transit and tape, and almost as accurately by means of the plane table, telescopic alidade, and stadia rod. For the measurement of many sections, however, this surveying precision may be unnecessary; indeed, it may give a false impression of exactness relative to natural variations in thickness and in lithology of the measured layers. This does not mean that sloppy procedures or inaccurate measurements are ever justified, but it should be emphasized that the control methods should be consistent, in terms of their accuracy, with the nature of the materials being measured. The best methods are the most rapid and flexible ones that will yield *reasonably* accurate results. What sense is there in measuring the thickness of a unit to the nearest tenth of a foot if its thickness is several inches less or greater only a few feet away?

The more precise methods require considerable computation, and great care must be taken to avoid calculating errors, even when a slide rule or a simple computer is used. The solutions also can be obtained graphically or through the use of nomographs, but these drawings must be large and accurate enough for detailed work. They may require as much time to manipulate as a slide rule. Methods of direct measuring, in contrast, are much simpler. The Jacob staff technique requires only a single notation, and the Hewett method only a single notation and a single calculation.

Sections ordinarily should not be measured in situations where the combinations of surface slope and dip of layers are highly complex or otherwise unfavorable. Favorable situations can be classified according to eight general combinations of slope and dip as shown in Fig. 3–36:

(a) surface horizontal to gently rolling, dip of layers horizontal to about 10°
(b) surface horizontal to gently rolling, dip of layers 10° to about 55°
(c) surface horizontal to gently rolling, dip steep to vertical, about 55° to 90°
(d) surface sloping from several degrees to about 40°, dip of layers horizontal to about 10°
(e) surface sloping from several degrees to about 40°, dip of layers in opposite direction from about 10° to about 55°
(f) surface sloping from several degrees to about 40°, dip of layers steep in opposite direction to vertical, about 55° to 90°
(g) surface sloping from several degrees to about 40°, dip of layers in same direction from about 10° to about 55° and slope angle greater than dip
(h) surface sloping from several degrees to about 40°, dip of layers steep in same direction to vertical, about 55° to 90°, and dip greater than slope angle

The last five combinations of slope and dip (*d-h*) become special situations when the slope angles are greater than about 40°; only in rugged mountainous country would it be necessary to measure sections on such slopes for considerable distances. However, rock layers along many canyon walls are well exposed in combinations of moderately steep slopes and vertical cliffs or ledges. Outcrops on the slopes can be measured in any of several ways, such as with a Jacob staff or by the Hewett method, whereas those on the cliffs can be measured directly by means of a weighted tape hung

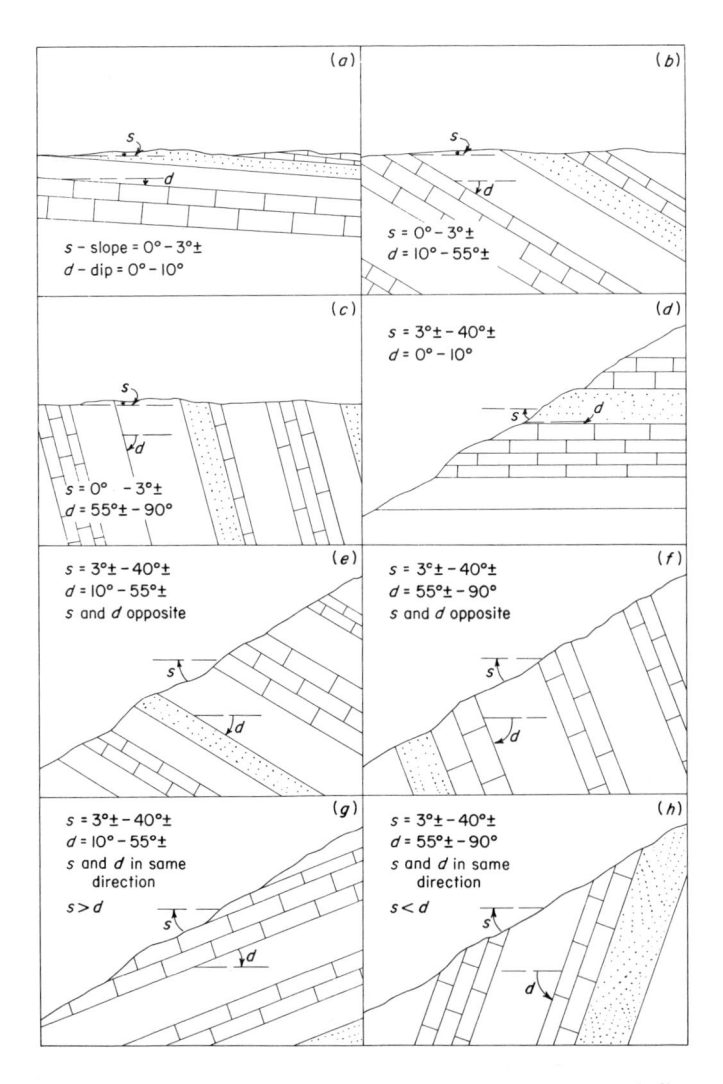

Fig. 3–36. General combinations of surface slope and dip of strata in situations where sections ordinarily are measured.

from above or by the scaling-off of thicknesses by the geologist as he climbs the cliff faces or chimneys in the back of the face.

In terms of a desirable balance among the factors of accuracy, time, equipment, manpower, and relations between slope and dip, the following techniques can be recommended, in order listed, for situations where it is possible to measure along a line normal to the strike of exposed units:

> For case (a) (Fig. 3–36), plane-tabling and compass-pace
>
> For case (b), Jacob staff, Hewett method with Abney hand level or Brunton compass, plane-tabling, compass-tape, and compass-pace
>
> For case (c), direct measurements (if layers are vertical), compass-tape, and plane-tabling
>
> For case (d), hand-leveling (if layers are horizontal), Jacob staff, Hewett method, and plane-tabling
>
> For case (e), Jacob staff, Hewett method, plane-tabling, and compass-tape
>
> For case (f), direct measurements (if layers are vertical), Jacob staff in against-dip direction, and compass-tape
>
> For case (g), Jacob staff and Hewett methods sighted slightly uphill, plane-tabling, and compass-tape
>
> For case (h), Jacob staff (in against-dip direction), and compass-tape

Other methods could be employed in some of these situations, but in general they would not be as satisfactory as those listed. Considering cases *d* through *h*, where the surface slope is steeper than about 40°, the recommendations are: for case (d), hand-leveling if the layers are horizontal, Jacob staff, Hewett method, and transit-tape; for case (e), Jacob staff, Hewett method, transit-tape; for case (f) and case (h), transit-tape; and for case (g), Hewett method (uphill) and transit-tape.

Where units must be measured along traverses oblique to the strike, the Jacob staff is of limited use, but the Hewett method, plane-tabling, transit-tape, compass-tape, and compass-pace techniques can be applied effectively. The transit-tape and Paulin altimeter methods are especially suitable for rugged, brushy country, even though the Paulin altimeter should be regarded mainly as a reconnaissance tool for checking measured sections. The determining of distances and bearings between points along a measured section, or between points at opposite ends of a section, by plotting them on a topographic map or on an aerial photograph is little more than a reconnaissance method. It is applied mainly to verify other measurements, to obtain much generalized information quickly, and to select sections for measurement in greater detail by other methods.

As indicated by the listed recommendations, the Jacob-staff method and the Hewett method (utilizing an Abney hand level or a Brunton compass) are first choices for measuring sections under most normal combinations of ground slope and dip of geologic units. Over vast parts of the United States, the surface is horizontal to gently rolling and the dip of layers is horizontal to inclined at low angles. Here the plane-table, compass-pace, and compass-tape techniques should be used unless there are numerous, well-distributed, steep exposures along road cuts, pit and quarry walls, and stream courses. Sections exposed on these steeper slopes can be measured directly by laying a ruler on the edges of the layers, they can be hand-leveled if the layers are horizontal, or they can be measured with a Jacob staff or by means of the Hewett technique.

The carefulness of field work is as important as the choice of a technique for measuring a section. As emphasized long ago by Hayes (1909) and recognized even in the present age of sophisticated instrumentation, the essential qualities of field observations are thoroughness, accuracy, organization, and comprehensiveness. All necessary measurements should be recorded, not left to memory, and they should be noted in a systematic way according to an outline or schedule. Close, careful measurements promote accuracy; all results should be double-checked. Strike and dip of rock layers should be verified frequently, lest control for the section be inaccurate owing to unrecognized shifts in attitude of the measured layers.

4 □ Types of Measurements

Mathematical types of measurements of rock layers are dependent only upon relations between slope of the surface and dip of the measured layers, as corrected from the direction and inclination of the traverse. Considering the inclination of the strata, there are four general situations: layers horizontal, layers vertical, layers moderately inclined, and layers steeply inclined, as well as sections where the strike and dip, or strike or dip are variable within short distances.

HORIZONTAL LAYERS

Measurement of horizontal layers involves merely the determination of differences in elevation between the bottom and the top surfaces of each unit defined in the section. Horizontal positions of the control points have no bearing on the calculation of thickness; they are plotted on a map solely to show where the section was measured.

Where the surface slope is moderate to steep (Fig. 3–36d), the swiftest method for measuring horizontal layers is hand leveling, using Jacob staff, Locke hand level, Abney level, or Brunton compass (Fig. 3–13). Horizontal layers exposed in vertical cliffs or as vertically faced ledges can be measured directly by a weighted tape; alternatively, their base and top can be located by means of a telescopic alidade or transit.

In contrast, horizontal or gently dipping beds cropping out along a gently rolling surface (Fig. 3–36a) pose a surveying problem that normally requires a plane table and alidade traverse or at least a compass and tape circuit. A compass-pace traverse may be reasonably accurate for thin units that form wide outcrop bands. Measurements are more easily made if exposures of the layers can be found in road cuts, along stream banks, or in walls of pits and quarries; such exposures can be hand-leveled to obtain thicknesses.

VERTICAL LAYERS

Vertical layers are not common even in structurally complex areas, although over large regions layered rocks may dip at high angles approaching 90°. The thickness of vertically dipping units, as measured normal to their strike, is simply the measured horizontal distance (Fig. 4–1). Elevation differences are used only to convert slope distances along the traverse to the horizontal distances.

Vertical Layers with Constant Strike

If the surface of exposure is essentially horizontal, the thickness of units can be taped across the surface, or the horizontal distance can be measured by stadia methods. As shown in Fig. 4–1, the inclination of the surface slope may require measurement for calculating the thickness of vertical units, even though true stratigraphic thickness is merely the horizontal distance measured perpendicular to the strike. The transit and tape and compass-tape techniques are best suited for such moderate to steep surface slopes. The horizontal distance H is found from the slope distance D and the slope angle s by the formula $H = D \cos s$.

Sections along ridges or in valleys that trend oblique

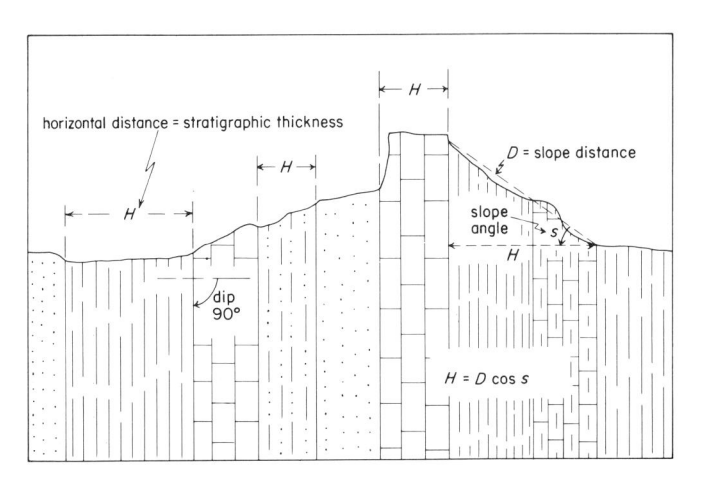

Fig. 4–1. Measurement of vertical strata in a direction normal to their strike.

to the strike of vertical layers with constant strike can be measured via offset traverses (Fig. 4–2), or they can be traversed continuously along a straight line oblique to the strike (Fig. 4–3). In the latter case, the distance normal to the strike is determined by the formula $H = Q \cos a$, where H is the horizontal distance normal to the strike and to the surfaces of the units, Q the horizontal traverse distance measured oblique to the strike, and a the angle between the traverse line and the line normal to the unit surfaces. If any part of the section is measured on a sloping surface, the H of Figs. 4–1 and 4–3, the horizontal distance normal to the strike and the stratigraphic thickness, is determined as previously noted from the slope distance D and the slope angle s.

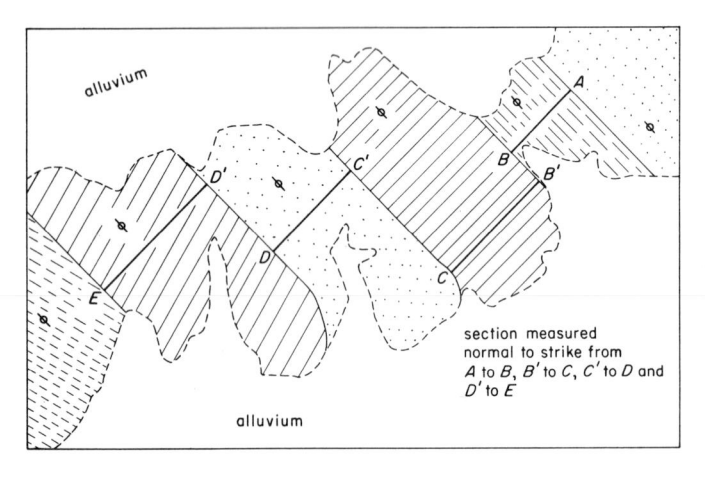

Fig. 4–2. Map showing measurement of vertical beds by offsetting along unit boundaries.

VERTICAL LAYERS

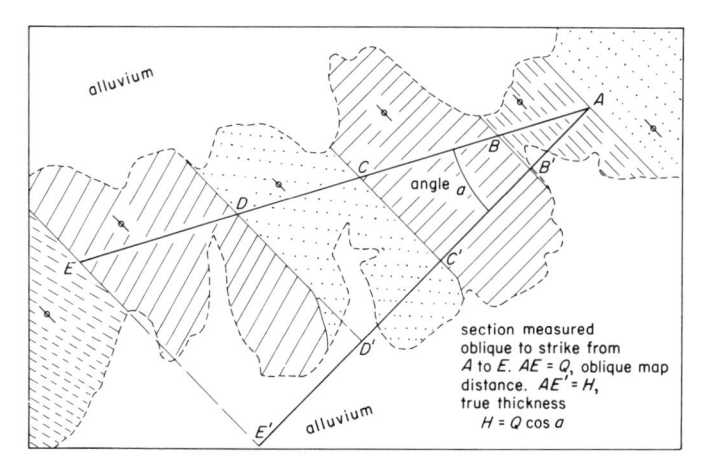

Fig. 4–3. Map showing measurement of vertical beds along a line oblique to strike.

Caption text in figure: section measured oblique to strike from A to E. $AE = Q$, oblique map distance. $AE' = H$, true thickness $H = Q \cos a$

Vertical Layers with Variable Strike

The strike and dip of layered units generally vary throughout any section-measuring traverse. If this variance is small, an average strike and dip can be determined for each measured unit or for two or more parts of a thick unit, and calculations of thickness then can be based on this average. When the horizontal distance in a direction normal to the calculated average strike is determined, it is the calculated stratigraphic thickness for vertical layers. This horizontal distance also is useful for measuring the thickness of inclined layers of known dip (Fig. 4–4), as the stratigraphic thickness can be calculated trigonometrically or determined from Table 2 in the Appendix.

![Figure showing calculation of thickness from horizontal traverse for vertical beds (left: dip 90°, H = stratigraphic thickness) and inclined beds (right: T = H sin d)]

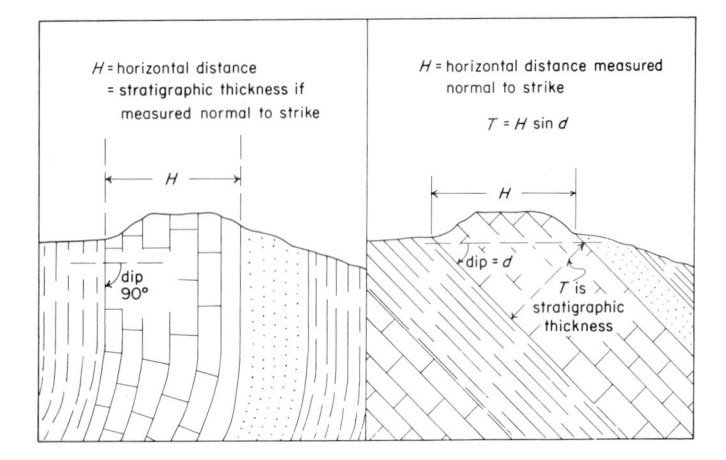

Fig. 4–4. Calculation of thickness from horizontal traverse for vertical and inclined beds measured along a line normal to the strike.

If there is considerable local variation in the strike of vertical layers, one method of averaging is to determine the strikes of many layers, plotting the readings carefully on a map or an aerial photograph—or even marking the points of observation on the outcrop with flags—and then measuring the horizontal distance in a zigzag series of lines (Fig. 4–5) from one boundary of the unit to the other. Each leg in the series is measured between the strike lines representing two adjacent points of observation, and is measured in a direction normal to a line representing the average of the two strikes. The total zigzag distance approximates the thickness of the vertical beds. The points of observation should be so chosen that they will form as straight a line as possible.

Two alternative graphic approaches have been sug-

VERTICAL LAYERS

gested by Low (1957, pages 279–282). These are the "average-distance" and the "average-bearing" methods, which are suitable only when the change in strike is even and gradual throughout the units measured. For the average-distance method (Fig. 4–6), strikes of vertical layers are determined at two points, the strike lines are projected from these points, and perpendiculars are drawn from each point to the projected strike line of the other point. The two perpendiculars, A–A' and B–B' in Fig. 4–6, are scaled from the plot, and half of their sum is taken as the average horizontal distance between the two points. This is the stratigraphic distance between them.

In the average-bearing method, strikes are measured at two points and their average is calculated. For example, in Fig. 4–7 the strike of layers at A is N. 10° E., whereas the strike at B is N. 20° W.; the average of these

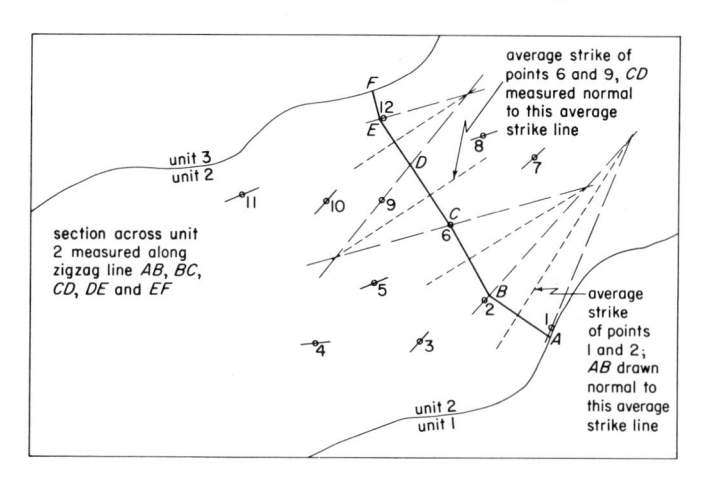

Fig. 4–5. Zigzag method of averaging variable strikes of vertical layers.

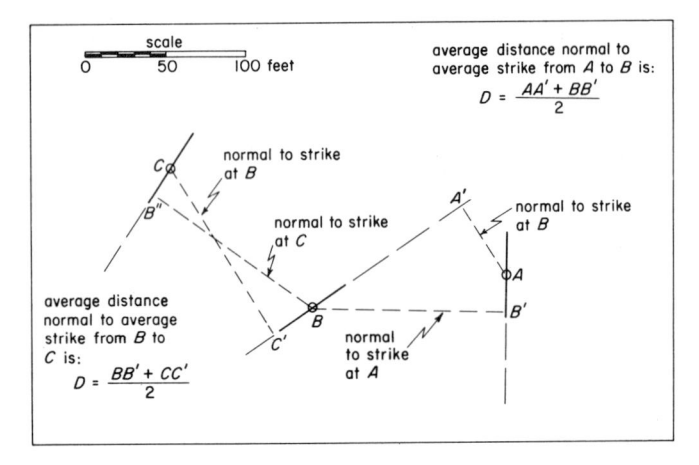

Fig. 4–6. Average-distance method for measuring vertical layers with progressively shifting strikes.

strikes is N. 5° W. Lines bearing N. 5° W. are drawn through both points, and the perpendicular between these lines is the horizontal distance normal to the average strike; this distance, representing the stratigraphic thickness, can be scaled from the plot.

In any of these measurements involving vertical strata, particular care must be taken in determining the horizontal distances, as any error translates to a proportional error in stratigraphic thickness. Plane-tabling or compass and tape techniques are best suited for such measurements over horizontal and moderately inclined surfaces.

INCLINED LAYERS

Layers that are oriented neither horizontally nor vertically are most commonly encountered in sections

INCLINED LAYERS

that require measurement. Except in situations with unusual combinations of surface slope and rock structure, the dip of layers, whether moderate or steep, does not affect the mathematical calculations for section control. The dip is pertinent, however, in determining the choice of the most effective measuring technique.

Inclined Layers with Constant Dip and Strike

Inclined layers with absolutely constant dip and strike are rarely encountered, but in many sequences either the variance is only a few degrees or the change in strike and dip is so gradual that each of the measured units can be regarded as constant in attitude. Indeed, essential constancy of strike and dip is a common criterion for defining a unit of a measured section, and a significant change in attitude may be reason for beginning a new

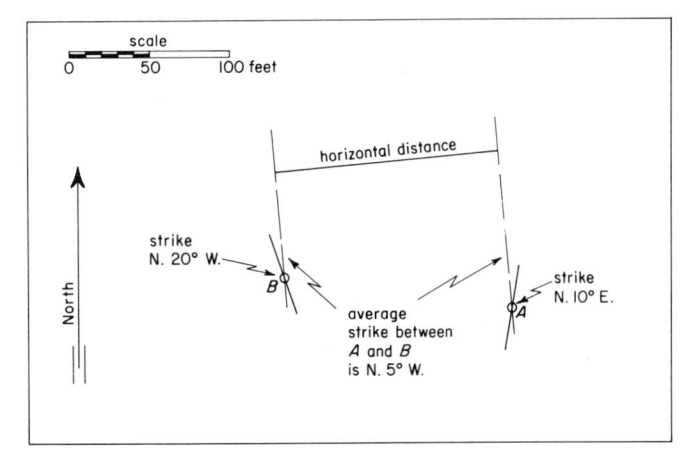

Fig. 4–7. Average-bearing method for measuring vertical layers with progressively shifting strikes.

unit. Numerous shifts in attitude are the rule rather than the exception, and highly precise surveying techniques cannot be wasted on sections where such shifts reduce the accuracy of calculated thicknesses to ranges of say 2 to 5 percent.

Calculated thicknesses of inclined layers with relatively uniform strike and dip depend in part on the relation of rock layers to surface slope. The measured elements of surface slope can be separated into two categories: (1) slope angle and slope distance, or (2) horizontal (map) distance and difference in elevation. The compass-tape technique, for example, is employed to measure the first pair of elements, whereas plane-tabling yields calculated values for the latter two. Strikes and dips of the layers must be determined in either case.

Inclined layers exposed on a horizontal surface Where the surface is essentially horizontal or is so gently rolling that average measurements of distance are horizontal, the two measured dimensions of inclined layers are their dip and horizontal distance perpendicular to their strike. Slope angles and vertical differences in elevation are so close to zero that they do not affect calculations. Stratigraphic thicknesses can be computed from the formula (Fig. 4–4) $T = H \sin d$, where T is the stratigraphic thickness, H the horizontal distance measured perpendicular to the strike, and d the angle of dip. Or, the true thickness can be determined from Table 2 in the Appendix.

In situations where it is not possible to measure the horizontal distances across thick units normal to their strike, parts of the units often can be measured in this direction but at different places, and then "tied together" by means of key layers or key beds. Alternatively, the layers can be measured along a line oblique to their strike, and the horizontal distance calculated from the cosine formula (Fig. 4–3) $H = Q \cos a$, where H is the horizontal distance, Q the traverse distance measured in a direction oblique to the strike, and a the angle between the lines representing H and Q. The true, or stratigraphic thickness of the unit can be computed directly by substitution of $Q \cos a$ for H in the formula for true thickness, obtaining $T = Q \cos a \sin d$.

Moderately dipping and steeply dipping beds exposed on horizontal surfaces are illustrated in Figs. 3–36b and 3–36c. For moderately dipping beds, measured normal to the strike, the Jacob staff method and the Hewett method are recommended, whereas the compass-tape and plane-table techniques are more desirable for situations where the layers dip steeply. For measuring oblique to the strike, the Hewett method is effective where the layers dip moderately; the plane-table and compass-tape techniques can be employed for any angle of dip.

Inclined layers exposed on a sloping surface In measuring inclined layers across a sloping surface, the slope of the surface affects the choice of measuring technique but not the basic mathematical computations. If the section is traversed in a direction perpendicular to the strike, four general situations can be defined:

1. surface slope and dip of layers in opposite directions, with the slope angle and dip angle totaling less than 90°
2. surface slope and dip of layers in opposite directions, with the sum of the two angles greater than 90°

3. surface slope and dip of layers in same direction, with the dip angle greater than slope angle
4. surface slope and dip of layers in same direction, with dip angle less than angle of surface slope

Situation 1 is shown in Figs. 4–8, 3–36e, and 3–29. Where the unit is measured in a direction perpendicular to its strike, and when S is the slope distance, d the dip, and s the slope angle as determined in the field, the stratigraphic thickness T is found from the formula $T = S \sin (s + d)$. If surveying instruments such as the plane table, telescopic alidade, and stadia rod are used, the determined elements are H horizontal distance and V vertical distance; the stratigraphic thickness then is given by the formula $T = H \sin d + V \cos d$ (Fig. 3–29).

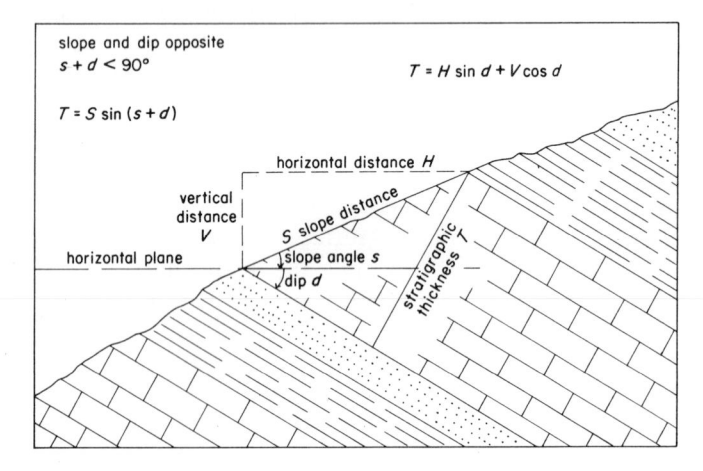

Fig. 4–8. Cross section of inclined beds on sloping surface with slope and dip opposite, their sum being less than 90°.

INCLINED LAYERS

Any of these simple problems can be solved graphically through the plotting of a cross section that shows the profile of the surface slope and the other measured elements; the stratigraphic thickness is then read off from the plot. If cross-section paper is used for such a plot, it should be rotated so that the boundaries of the units are parallel to one set of coordinate lines; then the stratigraphic thickness can be read directly along the other set of lines. To obtain plotting and reading accuracy within about half a foot, the scale of the cross section should be 10 feet to an inch. However, plotting of thick units to this scale requires large sheets of paper.

Recommended techniques for measuring units that dip in the same direction as the surface slope, and where the sum of the dip and slope angles is less than 90° (Fig. 3-36e), are the Jacob staff and Hewett methods, plane-tabling, and compass-tape method; where the layers dip steeply, say more than 55°, the latter two techniques yield more accurate results.

The general features of situation 2 are shown in Figs. 3-36f and 4-9. Where the stratigraphic unit is measured in a direction perpendicular to the strike, and where S is the slope distance, d the angle of dip, and s the slope angle, the stratigraphic thickness T is calculated from the same formula as that used for situation 1, $T = S \sin (s + d)$. Several other published formulas are more complex but indicate the relations of the measured elements more clearly. As illustrated in Fig. 4-9, $T = S \cos (s + d - 90°)$, and $T = S \sin [180° - (s + d)]$. Using trigonometric function relations, $\sin [180° - (s + d)] = \sin (s + d)$, so that $T = S \sin (s + d)$. Where a is any angle, $\cos -a = \cos a$, and hence $\cos (s + d - 90°) = \cos$

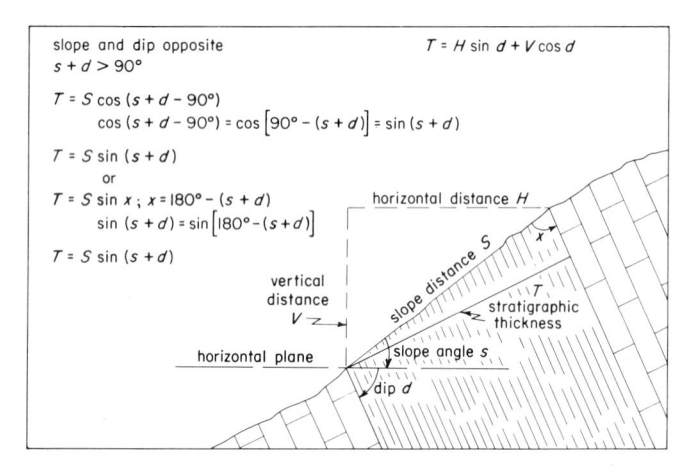

```
slope and dip opposite           T = H sin d + V cos d
s + d > 90°

T = S cos (s + d - 90°)
    cos (s + d - 90°) = cos [90° - (s + d)] = sin (s + d)

T = S sin (s + d)
    or
T = S sin x ;  x = 180° - (s + d)
    sin (s + d) = sin [180° - (s + d)]

T = S sin (s + d)
```

Fig. 4–9. Cross section of inclined beds on sloping surface with slope and dip opposite, their sum being greater than 90°.

[90° − (s + d)]; substituting via the trigonometric relation sin a = cos (90° − a), $T = S \cos(s + d - 90°) = S \sin(s + d)$.

If elements measured in the field are horizontal distance and difference in elevation, stratigraphic thickness is given as for situation 1 by the formula $T = H \sin d + V \cos d$. Recommended techniques for measuring are the Jacob staff method (in against-dip direction) and compass-tape; and where the slope is greater than about 40°, the transit-tape method.

Situation 3 is illustrated in Figs. 3–36h and 4–10. When the stratigraphic section is measured in a direction perpendicular to the strike, and where S is the slope distance, d the angle of dip, and s the angle of ground slope, the stratigraphic thickness T can be found from the formula $T = S \sin (d - s)$. Where surveying techniques such as plane-tabling yield horizontal distance H and vertical difference in elevation V, the stratigraphic thickness T is then computed from the formula $T = H \sin d - V \cos d$ (Fig. 4–11). Other measuring techniques suitable for this situation are the Jacob staff (in an against-dip direction) and compass-tape methods.

Situation 4, often referred to as "beds dipping out of the surface," is shown in Figs. 3–36g and 4–12. Where the section is measured in a direction perpendicular to the strike of layers, and where S is the slope distance, d the dip, and s the angle of ground slope, the stratigraphic thickness T is obtained from the formula $T = S \sin (s - d)$. When the vertical difference in elevation V

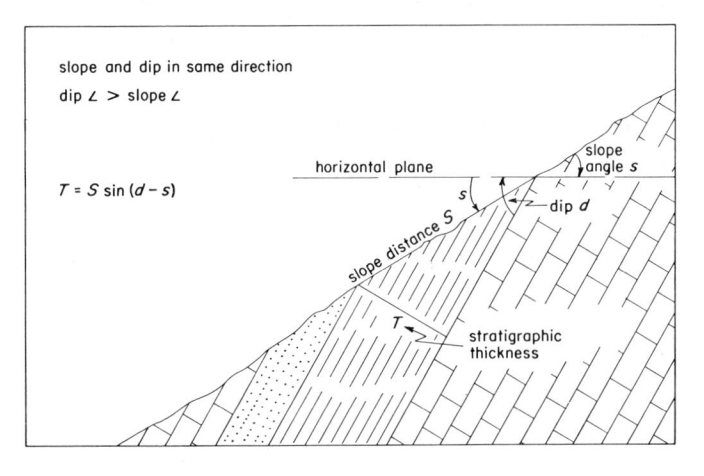

Fig. 4–10. Cross section of inclined beds on sloping surface with slope and dip in same direction, dip greater than slope, showing S and T relations.

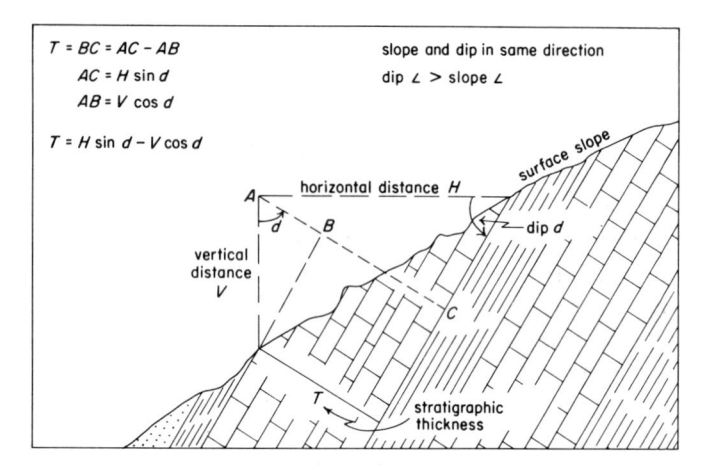

Fig. 4–11. Cross section of inclined beds on sloping surface with slope and dip in same direction, dip greater than slope, showing $T, H,$ and V relations.

and horizontal distance H are the measured elements, the stratigraphic thickness, for units measured normal to their strike, is given by the formula $T = V \cos d - H \sin d$ (Fig. 4–13).

Where layers "dip out of the surface," a situation not commonly encountered, the recommended measuring techniques are Jacob staff and Hewett methods (in an uphill direction), plane-tabling, and the compass-tape method. Where the layers dip more steeply than about 20°, the Jacob staff, Hewett, and compass-tape methods are awkward to use, so that plane-tabling is suggested instead.

When inclined layers are measured across a sloping surface in a direction oblique to their strike, *two* corrections (or conversions) are needed to find the stratigraphic thickness. One is to convert oblique slope distance *D*, as measured along the slope in a direction oblique to the strike, to the perpendicular slope distance *S* (Fig. 4–14). The other is to convert the slope angle σ in the vertical plane containing the oblique line of traverse to the slope angle *s* in the vertical plane perpendicular to the strike of the layers. In Fig. 4–14, if σ is the slope angle along the line of traverse, that is, the oblique slope angle, and *b* is the angle of divergence (between the oblique and perpendicular planes) in the horizontal plane, *s* the perpendicular slope angle is found from the formula tan *s* = tan σ/cos *b*.

Where angles *b* and σ are both less than 20°, angle *a*,

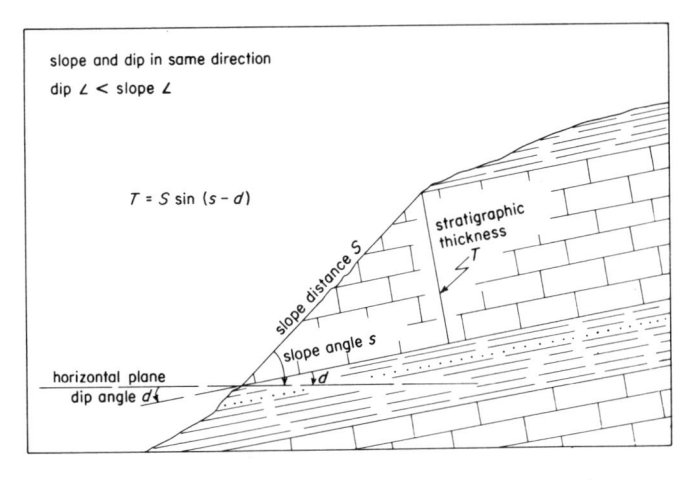

Fig. 4–12. Cross section of inclined layers on sloping surface with slope and dip in same direction, dip less than slope, showing *S* and *T* relations.

156   TYPES OF MEASUREMENTS

$T = BC = AC - AB$

$AC = V \cos d$

$AB = H \sin d$

$T = V \cos d - H \sin d$

slope and dip in same direction

dip $\angle$ < slope $\angle$

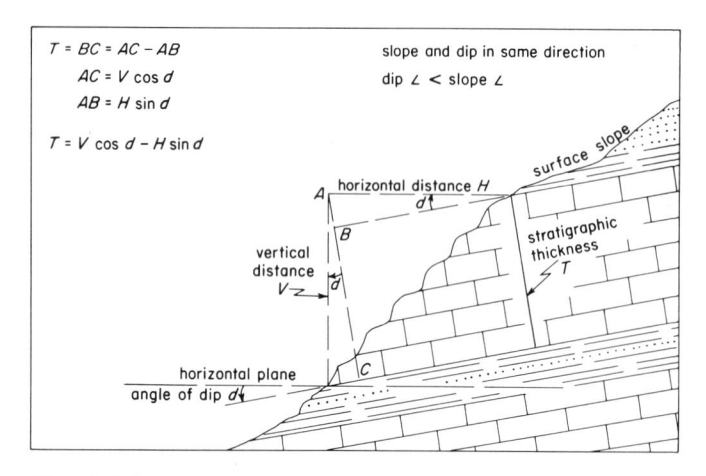

Fig. 4–13. Cross section of inclined beds on sloping surface with slope and dip in same direction, dip less than slope, showing T, H, and V relations.

$S = D \sin \sigma \csc \left(\arctan \dfrac{\tan \sigma}{\cos b} \right)$

$S = D \cos \sigma \sqrt{\tan^2 \sigma + \cos^2 b}$

$S = D \dfrac{\sin \sigma}{\sin s}$

$H = Q \cos b$

$\cos a = \dfrac{S}{D}$

$S = D \cos a$

$\tan s = \dfrac{\tan \sigma}{\cos b}$

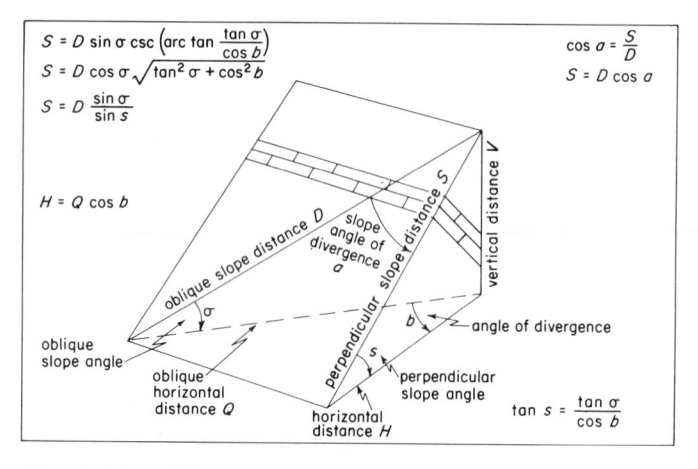

Fig. 4–14. Trigonometric relations of oblique and perpendicular measurements of inclined layers.

INCLINED LAYERS

the divergence angle on the surface slope, is almost equal to b. Using the formula $\sin a = \sin b \cos \sigma$, the following relations between a, b, and σ can be calculated, rounding off the sines and cosines to the nearest corresponding degree.

	\multicolumn{4}{c}{Angle b}		
	10*	20	30	40	
Angle a	10	20	30	39	10
	10	19	29	38	15
	9	19	28	37	20	Angle σ
	9	18	27	36	25
	9	17	26	34	30

* All numbers are given in degrees.

The perpendicular slope distance, S, can be determined approximately from the formula $S = D \cos a$; this is the S used in the preceding discussions of situations 1 through 4. Only where b, the actual angle of divergence, is small and hence not much larger than a, may this simple formula be used, as the angle of divergence *always* measured in the field is b. Also, S can be found, using D, σ and b, from various formulas, none of which is simple. The following are typical examples:

$$S = D \sin \sigma \csc [\arctan (\tan \sigma / \cos b)]$$
$$S = D (\sin \sigma / \sin s) \text{ if } s \text{ has been calculated}$$
$$S = D \cos \sigma \sqrt{\tan^2 \sigma + \cos^2 b}$$

The simplest formula for calculating stratigraphic thickness of inclined layers measured across a sloping surface is that derived by Mertie (1922): $T = D$ (sin σ cos

$d \pm \cos \sigma \sin z \sin d$), where T is the thickness, d the angle of dip, and z the azimuth of the line of traverse measured from the line of strike of the layers. As the azimuth is $z = 90° - b$, the relation between z and b is $\sin z = \cos b$, and Mertie's formula can be read $T = D (\sin \sigma \cos d \pm \cos \sigma \cos b \sin d)$.

For situations 1 and 2, where the surface slope and dip of layers are in opposite directions (Figs. 4–8, 4–9) and where the section is measured in a direction oblique to the strike of the layers, the two products within the parentheses of the preceding formula are added before being multiplied by D to obtain T. For situations 3 and 4, where surface slope and dip of layers are in the same direction and the angle of dip is greater or less than the slope angle (Figs. 4–10, 4–12), the formula is $T = D (\sin \sigma \cos d - \cos \sigma \cos b \sin d)$.

If the horizontal distance and vertical difference in elevation are the elements measured in the field, as through use of the plane table and telescopic alidade, the only correction that must be made when the line of traverse is oblique to the strike is to compute H, the horizontal distance parallel to the dip direction, from Q, the horizontal distance corresponding to the oblique traverse. This is given by the mathematical expression $H = Q \cos b$, where b is the actual divergence angle (Fig. 4–14).

For situations 1 and 2, where the surface slope and dip of layers are in opposite directions, the stratigraphic thickness is determined from the formula $T = Q \cos b \sin d + V \cos d$, with V being the vertical difference in elevation. For situation 3, where the surface slope and dip of layers are in the same direction and the dip angle

INCLINED LAYERS

is greater than the slope angle, the stratigraphic thickness $T = Q \cos b \sin d - V \cos d$. Where the surface slope and dip of layers are in the same direction and the dip angle is less than the slope angle, as in situation 4, the formula is $T = V \cos d - Q \cos b \sin d$.

Inclined layers exposed on a vertical surface In areas where sections must be measured along canyon walls, and where the more resistant layers crop out as vertical cliffs or ledges, it is necessary to determine only strike, dip, and the vertical distance V measured normal to the strike. As shown in Fig. 4–15, the stratigraphic thickness T is computed from the formula $T = V \cos d$. The vertical distance can be measured by a weighted steel tape carefully lowered down the face of the cliff, it can be scaled directly by traversing with a

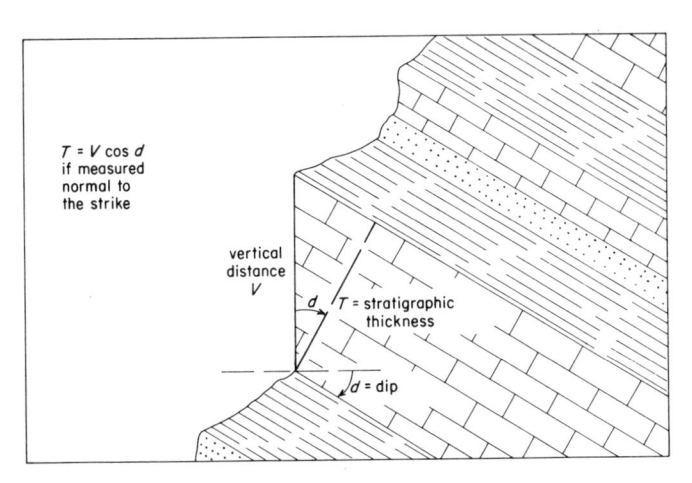

Fig. 4–15. Measurements of inclined beds along a vertical surface.

yard stick, Jacob staff, or tape held against the vertical wall along large joint cracks or chimneys, or it can be measured directly by offsets on the face of the cliff along the edge of talus piles.

Inclined Layers with Constant Dip and Variable Strike

The measurement of inclined layers with constant dip but variable strike is similar to that already described for vertical layers with variable strike. If the variations in strike are averaged by some mathematical or graphic method, a horizontal distance perpendicular to the average strike is determined. For vertical beds this perpendicular horizontal distance H is equal to the stratigraphic thickness, whereas for otherwise inclined layers the stratigraphic thickness T can be calculated by the formula $T = H \sin d$, where d is the dip angle (Fig. 4–4).

Three methods of averaging variable strikes, generally applicable to inclined layers, are the zigzag method (Fig. 4–5), the average-distance method (Fig. 4–6), and the average-bearing method (Fig. 4–7). Another, somewhat complex graphic method that was devised by Busk (1929) can be used with a plane-table traverse to measure a section characterized by constant dip and variable strike; this arc method has been illustrated by Low (1957, pages 292–294, Fig. 152).

In some instances variations in strike can be "absorbed" by splitting the section being measured into thin lithic units, each having a relatively small internal variance in strike. Each thin unit then can be measured in a direction perpendicular to the average strike of its component layers. The variance of strike within such

INCLINED LAYERS

units ordinarily is not great, so that essentially no error is introduced by using an average strike for each unit.

Inclined Layers with Constant Strike and Variable Dip

The simplest method for measuring inclined layers with a uniform strike and variable dip is to select thin lithic units within each of which the dip can be easily and accurately averaged, and to employ a different average dip for every unit if necessary. This is akin to the selection of units in a section with variable strike, as outlined in the preceding paragraph.

Where a section must be measured across poorly or partly exposed layers that vary widely in dip, it is commonly assumed that the dip varies uniformly between observed points. If dip readings can be taken where large changes in dip occur, at least three methods can be used to average the dips for calculations of stratigraphic thicknesses. The simplest and quickest method, which in general yields reasonably accurate results, is to average arithmetically the dips from two adjoining points of observation, and then to use this average value in computing the stratigraphic thickness between the points or in plotting a profile of the measured section and determining the thickness graphically (Fig. 4–16). In the graphic method, lines are drawn from two adjoining points according to the averaged dip, and the perpendicular between these lines represents the stratigraphic thickness.

The average-distance method (Hayes, 1909) is similar to the average-dip method but is mainly applicable where the ground surface is almost horizontal. Hori-

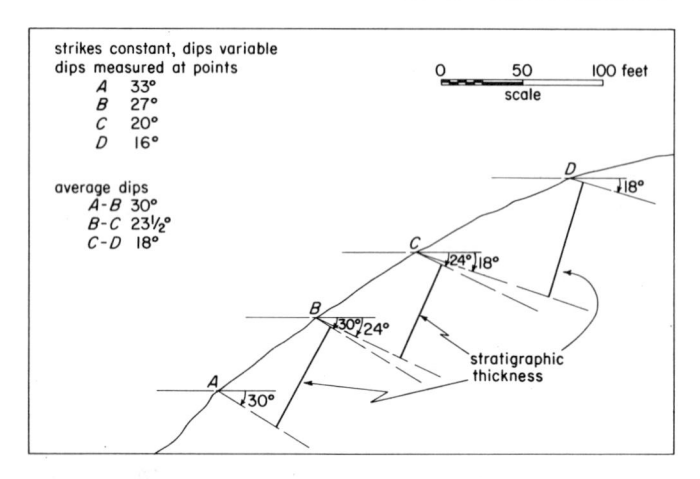

Fig. 4–16. Cross section showing graphic method for determining thicknesses from average values of dip.

zontal distances are measured, in a direction normal to the strike, between points where dips are determined. A profile is then drawn and the dips at each point are plotted and extended both above and below the line of profile (Fig. 4–17). A line is drawn perpendicular to the dip at each point, and is extended until it intersects the dip lines from the two adjoining points. Thus two dip normals are present for each pair of points, one above and one below the profile; the average of their lengths, as defined by the related dip lines, is taken as the stratigraphic thickness between the two points. For example, the stratigraphic thickness from A to B in Fig. 4–17 would be computed as one-half the sum of $Aa' + aB$.

The arc method of averaging dips, as outlined by Busk (1929), uses the graphic construction of circle arcs to

INCLINED LAYERS

average the stratigraphic thicknesses between points of contrasting dips. Dips are measured at points along a line perpendicular to the constant strike of the layers, and the horizontal and vertical position of each point is determined by plane-tabling or by some other suitable technique. A profile then is plotted (Fig. 4–18); at each plotted point the corresponding dip is laid off with a protractor, and perpendicular lines are erected and extended until they intersect the perpendicular lines from adjacent points. The intersections of these perpendiculars are then used as centers to draw arcs through the plotted points of observation. To illustrate this construction, *Aa* and *Ba* in Fig. 4–18 are perpendicular to the dip lines drawn through *A* and *B*, respectively, and they intersect

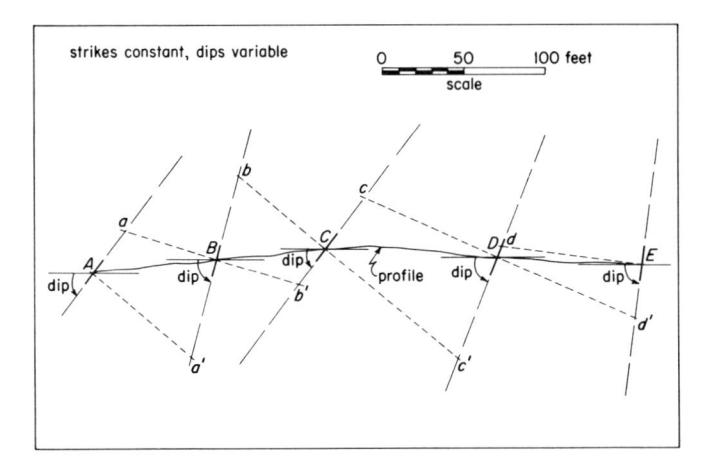

Fig. 4–17. Cross section showing graphic method for obtaining average thicknesses between points where dips are observed.

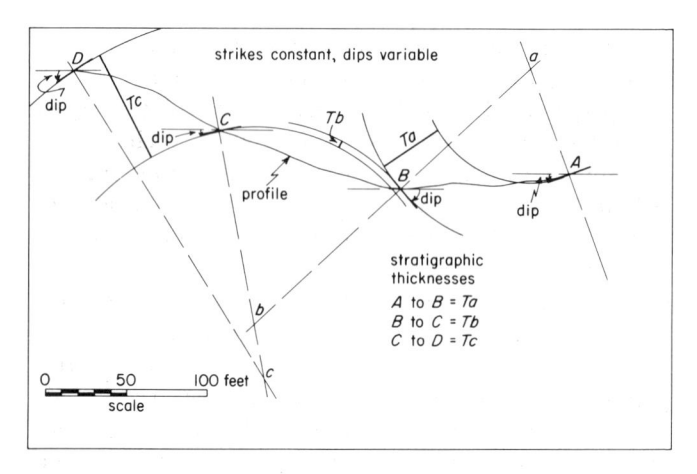

Fig. 4–18. Cross section showing graphic method to obtain thicknesses by means of pairs of concentric arcs.

at *a*. Using *a* as a center, arcs are drawn through the two points, *A* and *B*. The stratigraphic thickness is then measured along the radii between the adjacent concentric arcs, as *Ta* for the thickness from *A* to *B*.

If the dips between adjacent points differ by only a few degrees and if they vary uniformly between the points, the average-dip method is preferable to the other graphic methods and yields results that are at least as accurate.

Inclined Layers with Variable Strike and Dip

Where both strike and dip within a section are variable, it is desirable to break the section into lithic units or parts of units within each of which the strike and dip are uniform, or within each of which the variations in strike and dip of layers can be averaged by simple arithmetic or graphic means. As pointed out by numerous field geologists, the goal of stratigraphic measurements across units with variable strike and dip is to average the variations and to determine the stratigraphic thicknesses directly (as with a Jacob staff or by the Hewett method), or to measure the horizontal distance in a direction perpendicular to the average strike and then compute the stratigraphic thickness using an average value for the dip.

MEASUREMENTS PARALLEL TO THE STRIKE

Section measurements in a direction parallel to the strike of component layers are convenient in at least two common situations. As noted by Hansen (1960), the best exposures in the hogback or cuesta ridges typical in areas of tilted or folded layers commonly are not on the fronts or the backslopes of these ridges, but instead are found along the sides of water gaps or small across-strike valleys where the exposures have been swept free of talus. As these small valleys are cut normal to the strike in most places, across-strike measuring may be unfeasible if the valleys are floored with alluvium, but along-strike measurements can be taken on the valley walls. This can be done, for example, with a modified Jacob staff (Fig. 3–8) that has an auxiliary clinometer mounted normal to the forward level line of sight, and allows the geologist to tilt the staff sidewards to be normal to the plane of the layers' strike; thus the thicknesses of units can be viewed directly on the Jacob staff.

In canyon-scoured plateaus and mesa country, another common topographic situation, the best exposures for measuring sections generally are along the sides of small canyons. As Low (1957, page 297) has pointed out, the cliffs along many major canyons are too precipitous for detailed work and commonly are separated by steep talus-covered slopes; thus it is more practicable to measure sections along the sides of tributary canyons (Fig. 4–19). As the layers are measured by sighting parallel to the direction of strike but along a sloping traverse intersecting the plane of the layers' strike, the horizontal distance subtended by each unit enters into the calculations of thickness only if slope distances are used: commonly, the vertical difference in elevation and the dip are the necessary elements measured. For a dip angle d,

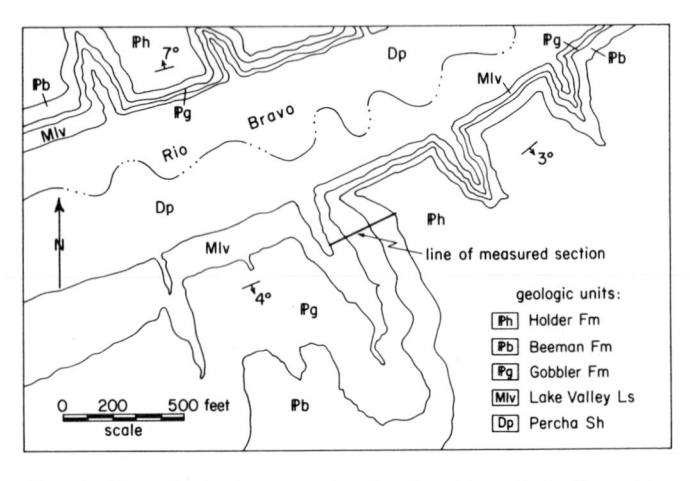

Fig. 4–19. Geologic map showing location of stratigraphic section measured in a direction parallel to strike of layers.

the vertical difference in elevation V is converted into stratigraphic thickness T, according to the formula $T = V \cos d$.

The vertical difference in elevation can be measured in several ways, and most rapidly by hand-leveling. A hand level, Brunton compass, or vertically held Jacob staff can be used. Plane-tabling may be satisfactory, but ordinarily involves many instrument setups owing to the high angles along most traverses. A Paulin altimeter traverse may be satisfactory for measuring thick, internally uniform units if the barometric pressure variations are not too great.

5 □ Errors in Measurements

Major errors in measuring of stratigraphic sections can be grouped into two categories, mechanical errors and errors of judgment, listed as follows:

1. Mechanical errors:
   a. misreading measurements such as of angles, taped distances, and stadia sights
   b. miscounting of items like paces and intercepts
   c. incorrect recording of data
   d. mistakes in scaling and plotting
   e. mistakes in computations
   f. errors in occupying points; for example, occupying the wrong point in making a traverse step, or not standing on a ground station in the way that gives correct vertical distance by the Hewett method

2. Errors of judgment:
   a. poor choice of measuring method for the topographic, stratigraphic, or structural conditions encountered
   b. assumption of parallel boundaries for measured units
   c. incorrect interpretation of covered intervals
   d. insufficient strike and dip control
   e. incorrect interpretation across faults or failure to recognize faults
   f. failure to distinguish true dips and strikes of stratigraphic successions from large-scale cross bedding or other layers with large initial dips such as those of fore-reef beds.

Errors such as miscounting the number of intervals measured or incorrectly occupying a sighting point may tend to be cumulative, and give an over-all greater or lesser thickness for units and for the entire measured section. Some errors, like slight misreadings of angles, taped distances, and stadia sights, may compensate each other; thus the over-all thickness of the measured section may be correct whereas some thicknesses of individual units may be slightly in error.

Errors in establishing control for measured sections are ascribable chiefly to incorrect determinations of distances and angles. The geologist first should assess the lithologic consistency of the rocks to be measured, as well as the structural features of the layers, then suit the accuracy of his control to these geologic conditions. Most layered rocks are variable in both thickness and lithology, and if a section is measured with an over-all error of not more than 5 percent, the control is sufficiently accurate relative to the natural consistency of the units that are measured.

PRECISION AND ACCURACY

Accuracy and precision are often defined as exactness and used synonymously, but accuracy does have the connotation of correctness, whereas precision is equated with mechanical exactness or reproducibility. This distinction is important in all scientific and engineering work, including the measuring of stratigraphic sections. An accurate or correct result cannot be obtained without precise measurements, but precision itself does not guarantee accuracy. A person might determine distances, for example, through careful, precise work with an old 100-foot tape, but if this tape actually were 102 feet long his measurements could not be truly accurate.

Accuracy is sought in the measuring of sections, but it rarely can be assessed in a practical way. Most calculations of errors deal with precision, but an approach to an evaluation of accuracy normally is made when sections are controlled by two or more different methods and the results are compared.

Both precision and accuracy are desired in measurements of thickness, but only in a few circumstances can the geologist expect results that are within 2 or 3 percent of the correct values. As noted from many published stratigraphic sections measured at the same localities by different persons, precision or reproducibility is only within about 10 percent of the extremes—and these are simple sequences of layers dipping at moderate or small angles, with essentially no structural complications. Assuming that the average thickness for a given locality is correct, the indicated accuracy of these measurements is within 5 percent of the true value. The measurements actually may be much more accurate, however, perhaps within 2 or 3 percent. The sections measured by different persons at a locality may have been traversed within a short distance of one another, but lateral thickness variations of the layers might be large within this distance and could cause a substantial part of the suggested inaccuracy.

Careful, precise, and systematic measurements should be made in the interests of accuracy, but the geologist also should use common sense in correlating his method with the situation. Employing a time-consuming and highly precise technique to a section in which the units are highly variable is unnecessary.

Through the use of surveying methods such as planetabling or transit-tape, and through repeated determinations of strike and dip in order to define structural variations within the rock sequences, a field party can measure many stratigraphic sections with errors of only 0.05 to 0.5 percent. The results of Jacob-staff traverses carefully made by several investigators have agreed within less than 3 percent (Robinson, 1959). Careful measurements with the Brunton compass, employing the Hewett method, should yield results reproducible within 2 to 5 percent. The purposes of the section measuring, as well as other factors such as accessibility and available time, funds, and personnel, generally govern decisions as to whether relatively precise but slower and more costly surveying techniques or more "rough and ready" methods are utilized.

MECHANICAL ERRORS

In the use of one-man instruments such as the Jacob staff, Brunton compass, and Abney hand level, the major sources of mechanical error are:

1. misreading dip and slope angles
2. misreading strike and traverse bearings
3. miscounting the number of measured intervals
4. mismeasuring horizontal or slope distances

The numerical data also may be recorded incorrectly, as with plane-tabling or transit-tape work, but fewer numbers are recorded and hence there is less chance of such errors. Slope and dip angles should be read with a precision of one degree; bearings also can be determined within a degree.

The most common sources of error in plane-tabling or in using transit-tape techniques are:

1. incorrect orientation of the instrument relative to earlier instrument stations
2. misreading the stadia rod
3. misreading angles recorded with the transit or misplotting directions determined with the alidade
4. miscalculation of trigonometric formulas
5. incorrect reading of numbers
6. inaccurate plotting of control points and
7. misreading strike bearings and dip angles

Careful work and simple checking will prevent out-and-out errors.

For a rapid check on possible cumulative errors, the beginning and ending points of the traverse can be plotted on a map, the horizontal distance and difference in elevation scaled off, and the stratigraphic thickness computed from the average strike and dip. If this calculation does not check the initial results of section measurement within 10 percent, computation, scaling, and plotting errors should be sought. If none is found, it may be necessary to re-run the traverse in order to identify other kinds of mechanical errors that probably were involved.

BOUNDARIES OF MEASURED UNITS

The methods and techniques outlined in this volume are based mainly on the assumption that each unit being measured is bounded by parallel surfaces. This assumption generally is valid if the locality for the measured section is carefully chosen. The measurement of layers enclosed by nonparallel surfaces is complicated and often inaccurate. Hewett (1920) and others have derived moderately intricate formulas for finding thicknesses of layers that are complexly folded and that therefore are bounded by nonparallel bedding surfaces. If possible, sections should not be measured in such structurally complicated areas.

COVERED INTERVALS

Even if section measurements are made carefully and precisely, serious problems may occur in the form of geologic uncertainties. Covered intervals, where layers of the section are concealed beneath surficial deposits, may include faults, zones of variable strike and dip, or significant elements of stratigraphic thinning or thickening (Fig. 5–1). Even with careful field work, it may not be possible to deduce true thicknesses in such situations; checking in adjacent areas commonly discloses outcrops of the units in question, but these exposures may be so far away from the main line of traverse that thickness and lithology are not representative of the concealed layers.

Covered intervals occur in nearly all areas where stratigraphic sections are measured. They should be

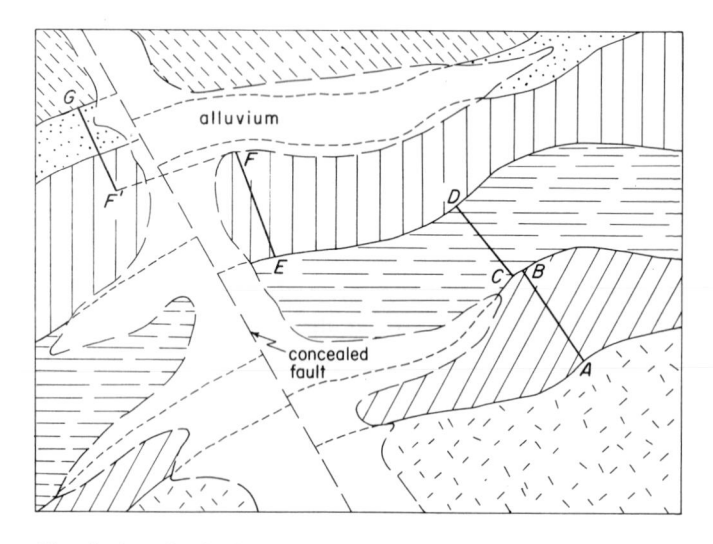

Fig. 5–1. Geologic map showing covered intervals concealing a fault and significant lateral changes in thickness. Section measured along traverses *AB*, *CD*, *EF*, and *F'G*, with error crossing fault from *F* to *F'*.

avoided wherever possible; where some must be included in a line of traverse, the covered intervals should be as few as is practical. They can be viewed as gaps in the available record, akin to lost samples in a series from a test hole. If covered intervals aggregate more than 10 percent of the section, it is poorly exposed.

Individual layers or groups of units are thinly concealed along many section-measuring traverses. Other sections are interrupted by much larger areas of thicker cover, such as wide alluvium-filled stream valleys and broad debris-mantled slopes. Satisfactory crossing of such large concealed intervals normally is a matter of correlating key layers and distinctive units from one side of the covered ground to the other (Fig. 5–1). This correlation must be done carefully, as any large structural or sedimentary changes that are hidden beneath the cover may cause huge errors in measured stratigraphic thickness, unless they are recognized and taken into account.

CORRELATION ACROSS FAULTS

More gross errors in thickness of measured sections are ascribable to the overlooking of faults or to incorrect correlation across faults than to any other factor. Owing to fracturing, crushing, shearing, and close folding, many fault zones are partly or wholly concealed by surficial deposits and are not easily recognized. Where they occur in lithologically uniform sequences or in sequences containing many layers that are lithologically similar, it is difficult to establish stratigraphic correlation across these breaks.

Lateral examination of outcrops near the measured section is useful insurance against overlooking faults.

The best method of detection generally is geologic mapping. Indeed, such mapping is a practical necessity in areas of complex structure, if the geologist wishes to avoid embarrassing stratigraphic duplication or omission in his measured sections.

Faults may be particularly difficult to recognize when measuring a composite section made up of scattered partial sections (Fig. 5-2), especially where the sequence contains many lithologically similar layers. For example,

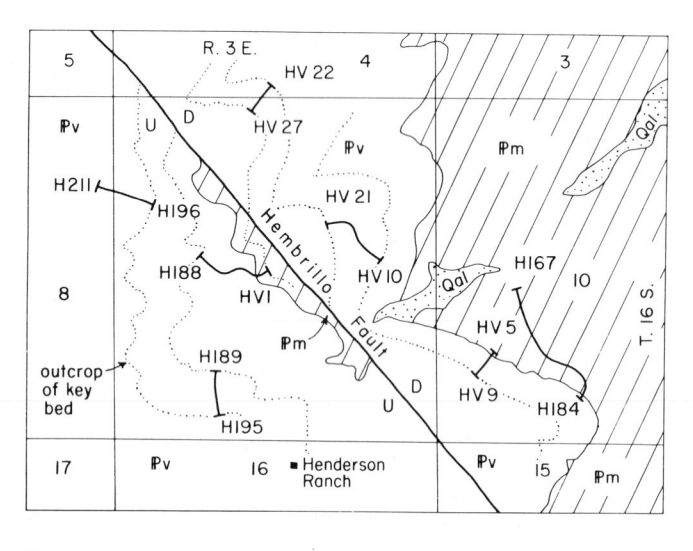

Fig. 5–2. Map of central San Andres Mountains, New Mexico, showing composite section traced across a fault zone.

the upper Pennsylvanian sequence in south-central New Mexico consists of alternating shales, sandy shales, sandstones, arenaceous calcarenites, and silty calcilutites. Cursory examination of a section in the central San Andres Mountains suggested only slight displacement along a fault zone. Subsequent detailed mapping, however, showed a stratigraphic displacement of 400 to 600 feet. The gross similarity of the sequences on opposite sides of the fault and abrupt lateral variations in some of these strata, within lateral distances of one half to one mile, are shown on Fig. 5–3.

In some situations one may not be able to correlate across a fault, especially when measuring detailed sections of lithologically uniform sequences; the investigator can only indicate the fault in his description of the measured section and list the assumptions made in the field.

OFFSETS IN SECTION TRAVERSES

Sequences that are to be measured are rarely exposed for long distances along a single, straight traverse line. After measuring a number of units, the geologist may find that higher layers are poorly exposed or entirely covered; the section then must be offset (Fig. 3–3) by tracing a suitable layer, unit, or group of units to a locality where the overlying units are satisfactorily exposed. Some possible errors due to offsetting across covered areas and faults already have been noted (Figs. 5–2 and 5–3).

If the offset can be walked out along a distinctive layer, there should be little chance of miscorrelation. If

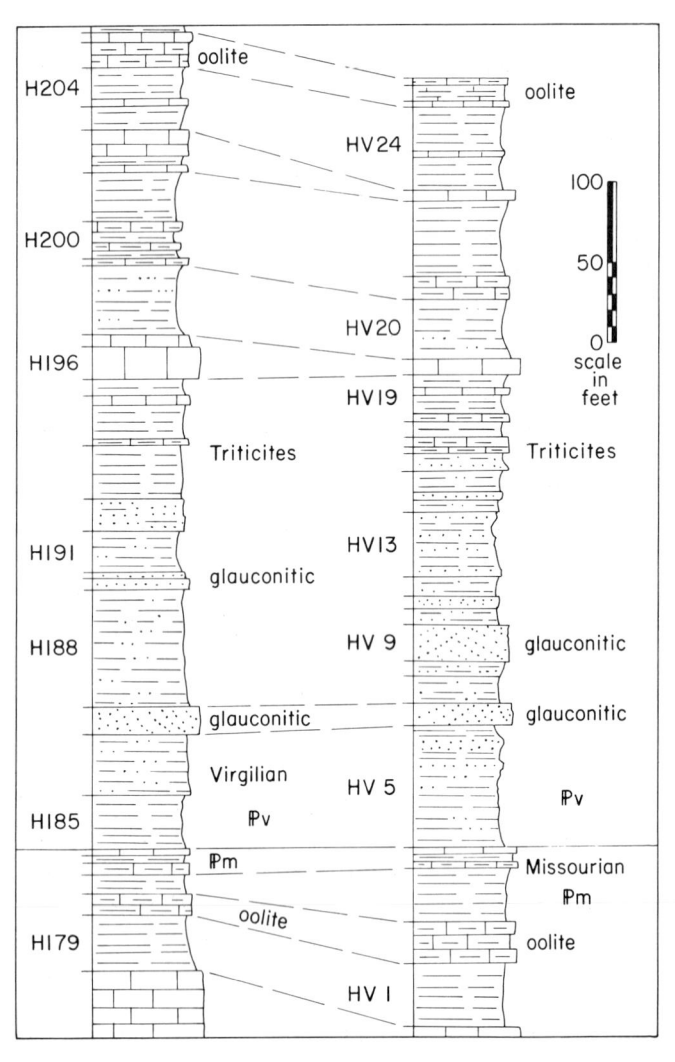

Fig. 5–3. Columnar sections and correlations of strata measured on both sides of fault zone shown on Fig. 5–2. Originally $HV25-27$ was believed to be correlative with $H180-182$.

the layer is unique in the sequence or is continuously exposed, there should be no stratigraphic error. However, if the offset involves a considerable distance, the thickness and lithology of the overlying units may be significantly different between the starting point and the end point of the offset. A comparison of thicknesses can be made by offsetting back to the original line of traverse at a higher stratigraphic horizon, particularly if other distinctive layers occur higher in the sequence.

If no distinctive key layers are present in the sequence being measured, offsets may be made by projecting a line of sight exactly parallel to the direction of the strike of the layers. Obviously, the projection must be done with great care or large errors in thickness may be introduced.

Offsets of sections across large covered areas such as broad, alluvium-filled valleys also should be made with extreme care to avoid errors. Key layers and other distinctive units provide the chief basis for correlating across such barriers; in addition, the units above and below these markers must be checked on both sides of the concealed area, since a series of unlike units is better than a single layer in establishing a firm correlation.

6 □ Description of Measured Units

Thickness has been emphasized in the foregoing discussions of section control, but it is only one of many significant parameters in the describing of sections. Full description of the measured units, and in some cases the sampling of these units, is at least as important for stratigraphic studies. Many volumes have been published on the characteristics of sedimentary and other layered rocks. Only the more pertinent descriptive features that should be recognized in the field can be mentioned in this manual.

In any description of layered rocks, a schedule of features to be observed is desirable for a complete systematic coverage of lithologic and other characteristics. A detailed schedule, such as that suggested by Twenhofel and Tyler (1941, pages 4–6), can be carried in the field for reference, but a simple outline of key items will serve most purposes. Tables or lists on which lithic features can be checked or described by means of symbols and key letters are useful.

The time and effort spent in describing rocks or other materials in the field depends in part on the purpose of measuring the section. If representative samples are collected from each unit and later are studied in the laboratory, field description can be reduced somewhat to emphasize gross lithology, bedding, weathering, topographic expression, and other features that are seen primarily at the outcrop. If only a few rock samples are collected, a more complete lithic description of the units should be made in the field. However, careful field observation is a necessary prerequisite even for later microscopic studies of samples.

Descriptions of layered rocks should follow standard classifications of the various features. For example, colors should be compared with, and named from, the *Rock-Color Chart* (Goddard *et al.,* 1951); listed grain sizes of clastic rocks should reflect some classification in common use (for example, Wentworth, 1922); limestones should be named according to a regular classification (for example, Folk, 1962; Dunham, 1962); and pyroclastic rocks can be described according to well-established categories (Wentworth and Williams, 1932). For many features, such as bedding and crystallinity, contrasting classifications have been suggested by various geologists, and choice among them is largely a matter of personal preference guided by the purposes of the study.

In addition to written notes describing the various lithic features, a sketched columnar section should be prepared in the field, in order to illustrate the gross outcrop features and complement the written description. The amount of writing can be further reduced through the use of common abbreviations (see Appendix Table 4). It is strongly recommended that written notes follow a definite schedule, as they will be relatively easy to use in subsequent work if their arrangement is systematic. Further, they can be expanded or shortened as necessary in describing unusual features, or units that lack distinctive features. Lateral variations also can be noted. Well-prepared check lists are an attractive alternative to notes, as they are easily and rapidly used in the field and may ensure that most features of possible significance are recorded.

SEDIMENTARY ROCKS

Systematic descriptions of sedimentary rocks can be based on a check list, a schedule of written notes, or some combination of these, generally accompanied by sketched columnar sections. A typical loose-leaf check list for outcrop description (Wengerd, 1955) is shown in Fig. 6–1. This is a brief tabulation of the more important lithic features, with the pertinent descriptive terms to be circled in the field, and is intended for use when representative samples are collected from each unit, these samples to be examined later under a binocular microscope. Each unit is described on a single sheet; the field description of the total section thus is a sheaf of loose-leaf pages.

A more detailed check list compiled by Roy W. Foster is shown in Fig. 6–2. Items such as particle size, round-

LOOSE SHEETS OUTCROP DESCRIPTION

PAGE _____

AGE _____
LOC _____
THICK _____
SAMP _____

CLASSIFICATION

CONGL QZITE SS SILT CLAY LS DOL GYP ARK GRWKE

COLOR

RED MAROON GREEN PURPLE YELLOW BUFF TAN BROWN BLACK GRAY

STRUCTURE (BEDDING)

MASSIVE MEDIUM THIN SHALY FISSILE

GRAIN SIZE

COURSE MEDIUM FINE VERY-FINE CRYPTO

ROUNDNESS

ANGULAR SUBANGULAR SUBROUND ROUND

SORTING

GOOD FAIR POOR

FOSSILS   TYPES

ABUNDANT MODERATE TRACE   BRACH PELECY GASTRO TRILO CRIN FUS COR

MODIFICATIONS

CONG SANDY SILTY CLAYEY LIMY SIL QZITIC ARK FELD OOLITIC
CHERTY MICACEOUS NODULAR GLAUC BRECC FRAG CALCAR

WEATHERING AND OTHER DESCRIPTION

Fig. 6–1. Loose-leaf check list for outcrop description (Wengerd, 1955).

183

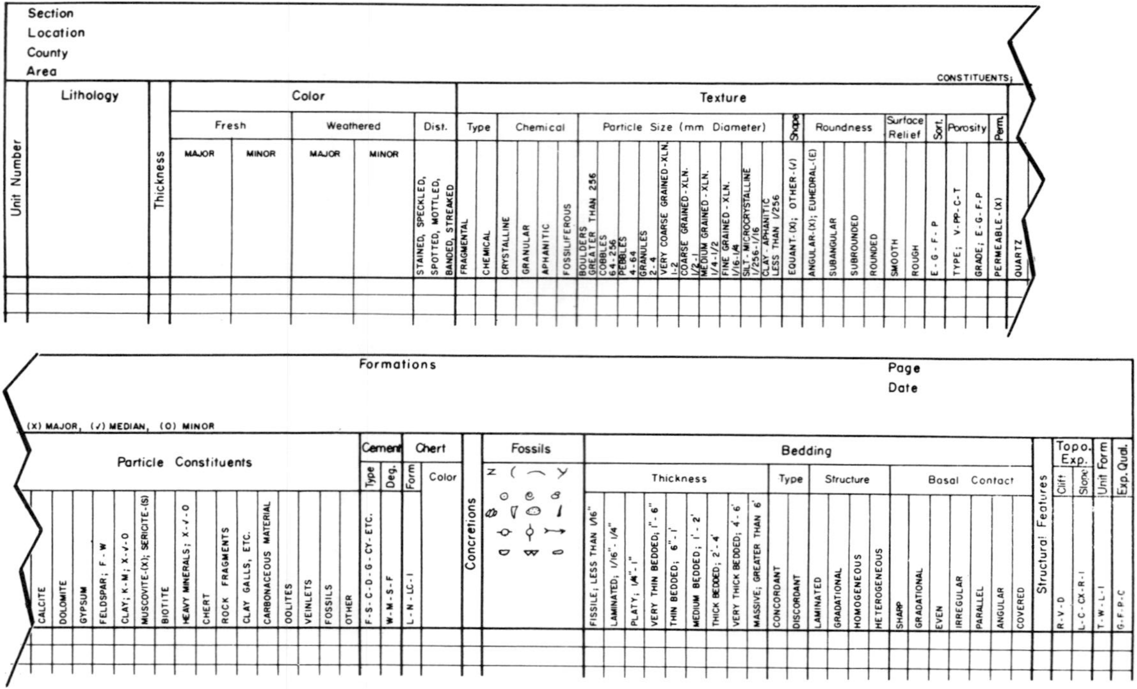

Fig. 6-2. Tabular check list for field description (by Roy W. Foster). Upper strip is left side of form; lower strip is the right side.

ness of clastic grains, particle constituents, and bedding are checked according to what is observed at the outcrop. Key letters are recorded for other parameters such as sorting (E—excellent, G—good, and so on), porosity, cement, and topographic expression. Descriptions of major items such as lithology, color, and fossils are either abbreviated or indicated by means of key symbols. On this check list, with dimensions of 7 × 13 inches, 40 units can be described; space is left at the bottom of the sheet and on the back for written descriptions of unusual features, lateral variation, and other pertinent characteristics.

A simpler form, adapted by Proctor (1961) from H. J. Bissell, is shown in Fig. 6–3. This is a combination columnar section and schedule for abbreviated description intended for use in the field and is not a check list. Lithology, topographic expression of the units, and occurrences of fossils are shown in the graphic section, whereas other features are recorded in the adjacent columns.

Other check lists and columnar schedules have been devised to suit various purposes in measuring stratigraphic sections, it being a simple matter for the geologist to make up his own form according to the needs of a given project. A form that is simple and adaptable to many uses is illustrated in Fig. 6–4. The headings on this form—unit number, feet, rock type, and general description (color, grains, cement, beds, structures, weathering, topographic expression, fossils, and sample number)—can be inked at the top of each page of a field notebook, or they can be printed commercially on lined sheets in a pad that is carried on a clip-board in the field. Along with the written description, a columnar

186 DESCRIPTION OF MEASURED UNITS

SECTION Wasatch Fm.					DATE 5/11/59	
LOCATION Cedar Breaks					COUNTY Iron Co, Utah	
Sec. 2 Twp. 37S. Rge. 9W.					Geologists: H. Bissell & P.D. Proctor	
UNIT NO.	FEET SMPL. ( )	OUTCROP; FOSSILS ▭Thin ⌒Fusul. ▭Med. ✱Bryoz. ▭Thk. ▽Brach. ▭Mas. ⊙Crin. ↻Other	COLOR Fresh / Weath.	TEXTURE Detr. or Xln. 2-1 mm.V.cs. 1-0.5 Cse. 0.5-.25 Med .25-.125 Fine <.12=VF;Mic.	POROSITY Vug.; Interg.; Inter x in.; P. pt.; etc. Good Fair } % Poor Dense	ADDITIONAL NOTES Mode of Weath. (blocky, slabby, etc.) Type & % chert (▲bedded; △nodular) Modifiers (aren., argil., calc., silic., etc.). Matrix, Detr., Skel., Biochem. (or combinations) Fossil types, abund. & arrangement
1		↻	5G 6/1 / 5B 5/1	0.5-0.25	Vug.10%	Blocky; 10% chert
2			5YR 8/4 / 5YR 7/2			
3	(42)		5YR 3/4 / 5YR 4/4	0.25-.12	25%	Slabby
4		↻	5B 5/1 / 5B 7/1	<0.12	P.pt.<5%	Platy, aren.
5		↻	5YR 5/6 / 5YR 5/2	1-0.5	Vug.15%	Blocky; silic.; gastrop.

Fig. 6–3. Combination columnar section and descriptive field form for recording stratigraphic data (Proctor, 1961).

section of the described units should be sketched either on the back of the preceding page or along the left side of the page. The section can be shown as a vertical column or in a form that reflects the actual surface profile (Fig. 6–5). The profile sketch provides a more complete visual summary of the written information.

The major features of sedimentary rocks (including many features applicable to igneous and metamorphic rocks) that should be described during the measurement of a stratigraphic section are:

1. rock type
2. minor constituents

SEDIMENTARY ROCKS

3. color on fresh surfaces
4. grain size, rounding, shape, sorting, and (or) crystallinity
5. cement and porosity
6. bedding
7. sedimentary structures
8. weathering characteristics
9. topographic expression
10. fossils
11. relations to adjacent units
12. thickness of the measured unit including lateral variations

Only those features that can be seen with the unaided eye or with a hand lens can be described readily at the outcrop, but the *careful observer can define* a remarkable

SECTION Robledo Mountain			FORMATIONS Penn. undif.
LOCATION NE¼ Sec. 35, T. 21 S, R, 1W.			BY F. Kottlowski
COUNTY Dona Ana, N. Mex.			DATE 7/25/52 p.42
UNIT NO.	FEET	ROCK TYPE	COLOR, GRAINS, CEMENT, BEDS, STRUCTURES, WNG., TOPO, FOSSILS, RS
RM1	1½	Sh, calc	yel-bn, platy, partly baked by sill; slope
2	1½	Ls	dk.gy.fn-xl, 1 irreg.bd; chert flakes; brachs, crin, bryoz; RS 441-219
3	2	Ls, carb	blk, dense, sh partings; laminated l & d, thn.-bdd, wrs dk gn; thn. ledges; fraqs. RS 441-220 of fos.
4	2	Sh	gy, wrs gn-gy, fissile; fossil molds; slope
5	3	Ls	bn-gy, fn-grd; hard irreg bds, 3 9" thk; rdd ledges
RM6	2½	Ls, arg	gy, wrs gn-gy; dense; lam. l & d, 6" bds, irreg ledges, fraqs brachs, crin; RS 441-221
7	1½	Sh, calc	gn-gy. fissile; 50% nod arg Ls; slope
8	1	Ls, silc.	lgy spotted gn; dense, 1 ledge; top nodular
9	9½	sh, calc.	gn-gy, 30% nod arg Ls; fossil molds; slope
RM10	2	Ls	gn gy, md-xl, 1 prom ledge, lam l & d; fusys; FS 441-222
11	4	Ls, arg	gy, dense, nodular with sh lam; slope and thn ledges

Fig. 6–4. Schedule form for description of units in measured section.

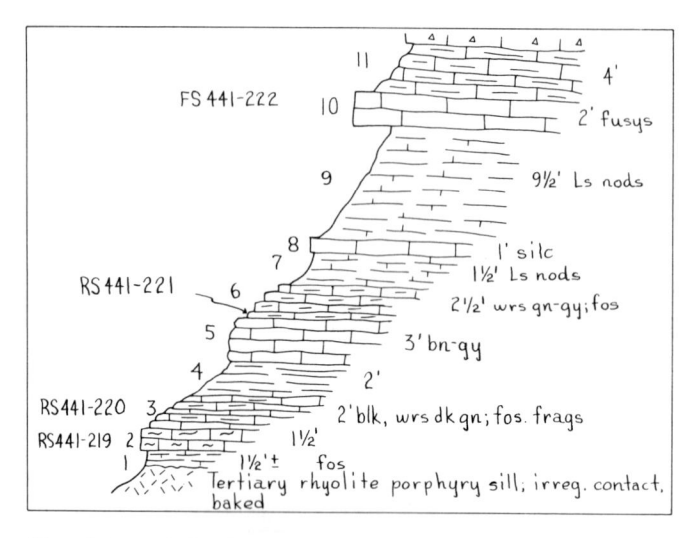

Fig. 6–5. Field-sketched profile and section of units described in Fig. 6–4.

number of characteristics *without recourse* to laboratory methods and equipment.

Rock Types

The dominant sedimentary rock types can be divided (Pettijohn, 1957, pages 191–194) into three categories: clastic rocks, carbonate rocks, and nonclastic rocks other than carbonates. Clastic rocks are those composed mainly of fragments of quartz or other silicate minerals, and therefore can be called siliciclastic rocks (Braunstein, 1961). They contrast with the carbonate rocks that are made up of clastic fragments, which are then termed calciclastic rocks. In general, the siliciclastic fragments are extrabasinal whereas the calciclastic materials are intrabasinal.

Siliciclastic rocks can be subdivided into three major groups based on grain-size diameters: (1) conglomerates and breccias, with clasts larger than 2 mm, (2) sandstones, with grains between 2 mm and 1/16 mm, and (3) siltstones and shales, with grains smaller than 1/16 mm. Further subdivision can be based on smaller ranges of grain size, on composition of the fragments, on the type of cement, and on presence of minor minerals.

The names of conglomerate and breccia are prefaced, according to clast size, by terms such as boulder, cobble, pebble, or granule. In addition, compositional terms yield names such as quartz pebble conglomerate and andesite cobble conglomerate. Names based on the nature of the cement or matrix include, for example, siliceous conglomerate, arkose conglomerate, and ferruginous conglomerate. Special types are tillite, intraformational conglomerate, cataclastic breccia, and volcanic breccia.

One of the most frequently used of the many classifications of sandstones (see Klein, 1963, for a review of sandstone classification) is that suggested by Pettijohn (1957, page 291); it is shown in modified form in Fig. 6-6. The major classes are graywacke (matrix rich in silt and clay), arkose (rich in feldspars, but with relatively little matrix), lithic sandstone, and quartzose sandstone (Pettijohn's orthoquartzite). Tuff and tuffaceous sandstone are pyroclastic or mixed deposits within the sandstone grain-size range. Examination of the rock under a binocular microscope may be required to identify the matrix and to properly name the rock. For

cement or detrital matrix		detrital matrix >15% cement absent	variable volcanic fine ash	detrital matrix <15% voids empty or filled with chemical cement			
sand or detrital components	feldspar exceeds rock fragments	feldspathic graywacke	(feldspars and other minerals) crystal tuff	arkose	feldspathic sandstone	quartzose sandstone	chert <5%
	rock fragments exceed feldspar	graywacke	lithic tuff vitric tuff	subgraywacke	lithic sandstone		chert >5%
	quartz	variable	variable	<75%	75-95%	>95%	

Fig. 6–6. Field classification of sandstones (modified from Pettijohn, 1957).

example, the distinction between a feldspathic graywacke and an arkose depends on whether the matrix is composed of very fine-grained material that may need to be differentiated under a microscope.

Fine-grained siliciclastic rocks are called claystone if of indurated clay-size grains, siltstone if of indurated silt-size grains, and shale if they are laminated or fissile claystone or siltstone. Grain-size analyses of claystones show that many contain as much as two thirds silt-size grains. Only when the contained silt amounts to about 70 percent of the rock, does its gritty feel become apparent.

The purposes of the study will determine which one

of the numerous classifications of carbonate rocks (see Ham, 1962) will be utilized. From a mineralogical viewpoint, carbonate rocks can be subdivided into limestone (90 percent or more calcite), dolomitic limestone (10 to 50 percent dolomite), calcitic dolomite (10 to 50 percent calcite), and dolomite (90 percent or more dolomite). Detailed identification of the complex carbonate-rock textures and constituents requires at least some laboratory work with thin sections, polished sections, etched surfaces, and transparent peels (Ham and Pray, 1962). Field techniques include small-scale acid etching and examination of a wetted, freshly broken surface with a hand lens.

The modern carbonate-rock classifications are too complex to be adequately presented simply or by a single chart or table. Before being able to utilize them in the field, the investigator must become familiar with their many details. Among the classifications most used are those of Folk (1959, 1962), Dunham (1962), and Leighton and Pendexter (1962). The major elements of Folk's classification are allochems (oolites, pellets, fossils, fossil fragments, and intraclasts), sparry calcite cement (clear calcite with grain size larger than 4 microns, 0.004 mm), and micrite (microcrystalline calcite ooze with grains 1–4 microns in diameter).

Dunham's system is subdivided into four major groups (mudstone, wackestone, packstone, and grainstone) based on the relative proportions of the coarser clastic particles (grains) and the finer matrix or lime mud, as well as on whether the lime mud forms the essential framework of the rock. Leighton and Pendexter's textural classification of limestones is based on the relative proportions of grains (detrital, skeletal, coated, pellets, and lumps) to micrite (upper limit is 0.03 mm) and on the type of limestone grains or framebuilder.

Nonclastic sediments other than chemical limestones are not as common, but they include some commercially important rocks. The most abundant of these are chert and other siliceous sediments, ironstones, phosphorite, coal, and evaporites such as rock salt, gypsum, and anhydrite.

Minor Constituents

Most sedimentary rocks are mixtures of at least several constituents. The dominant material defines the rock type, whereas the more abundant of the other constituents typically are listed as descriptive adjectives. For example, a limestone containing a minor amount of clay minerals is called an argillaceous limestone, and a sandstone with about 10 percent feldspar grains is termed a feldspathic sandstone. With respect to composition, it is useful to distinguish between mineral and chemical designations. A cherty limestone (Fig. 6–7), for example, contains chert in the form of discrete bodies, such as nodules, laminae, and stringers, whereas a siliceous limestone is one in which silica is intimately distributed throughout the rock. A ferruginous shale contains various interstitial iron-bearing minerals disseminated throughout, whereas a pyritic shale has scattered crystals of pyrite.

Often the importance of minor constituents cannot be assessed when measuring a section. Any that can be identified should be listed with a percentage estimate of their abundance. Common minor minerals in sandstones, for example, include micas, feldspars, carbonate minerals,

SEDIMENTARY ROCKS

Fig. 6–7. Cherty crinoidal calcarenite.

glauconite, and various heavy minerals, such as zircon and tourmaline. Most of these constituents can be identified at the outcrop by an observant geologist using a hand lens. Where grains are too small or too sparse for identification, or where their properties are not distinct enough to permit a specific designation as to species, they should be noted in terms such as, "less than ½ percent yellow-brown tablets, averaging 1 mm long—sphene?" and "about 1 percent femags in equant, subrounded grains." Fig. 6–8 is one type of chart that can be used to estimate percentages of accessory minerals on the outcrops or in a hand specimen.

Color on Fresh Surfaces

Color is one of the most obvious characteristics of any rock, but its description is not always a simple matter. It should be observed on freshly broken surfaces that

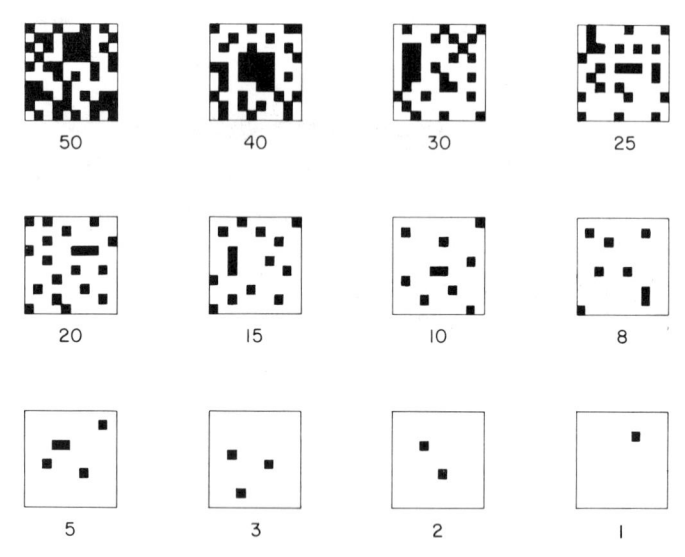

Fig. 6–8. Charts for estimating percentages of rock components.

represent parts of the rock unaffected by weathering, and also should be described for typical weathered surfaces.

For many objectives of section measuring, common color terms may be used, such as light gray, pink, dark green, and black. Many terms of this kind, however, mean significantly different things to different people. What is pale orange to one observer may be called pink by another. Further, slight actual changes in color within a rock unit commonly indicate corresponding changes in constituent mineral grains, cement, texture, or other properties.

Thus it is desirable to describe colors precisely in

most detailed studies of stratigraphic units. This can be done by comparison with color charts; the *Rock Color Chart* (Goddard et al., 1951), distributed by the Geological Society of America, includes small color chips that can be compared directly with rocks in the field or in the laboratory to obtain a fairly reproducible identification. This chart lists not only color names, such as moderate pink or light olive brown, but also the Munsell designations, which represent a numerical shorthand scheme for defining hue, value, and chroma. Light olive brown, for example, can be listed as 5Y 5/6, meaning a hue of 5Y (mid point of yellow), a value (of lightness) of 5, and a chroma (degree of saturation) of 6. Thus the observer, using the rock color chart, can record the Munsell number in lieu of writing the color name.

If colors of a rock sequence fall within a few Munsell divisions, a color graph (based on the value of the particular color) can be drawn to show the minor color modifications (see Fig. 2–7).

Color patterns of rocks vary from a single uniform color, to those with gradual internal shifts in colors, or those with two or more distinct colors, such as the "salt and pepper" coloring of light gray speckled with black, typical of rocks like quartzose sandstones containing scattered dark grains (or of dark mafic minerals scattered throughout a gray andesite), and to those with irregular distinct patterns, such as mottled, streaked, stained, spotted, speckled, or banded.

Grains and Crystallinity

Grain size is a primary basis for naming clastic rocks and is a most important textural feature related to their distinction and their genesis. The useful particle-size classification of Wentworth (1922) is shown as a guide in Fig. 6–9. Particles of granule or larger size can be measured directly with a scale, whereas the sand and silt sizes are best determined by comparison with a chart or a series of reference samples. Series of grain samples for comparison have been prepared by many organizations; an example is the sand-gauge folder (Fig. 6–10) available from the Geological Specialty Company of Oklahoma City.

Roundness of grains, which is mainly a function of their hardness, size, and geologic history, is related to the sharpness of their corners and edges. Roundness should not be confused with sphericity, which refers to gross particle shape. Various charts have been set up

size		sedimentary		pyroclastic	
mm	inches (approx.)	fragment	rock	fragment	rock
256	10	boulder	boulder conglomerate	bomb or block	agglomerate or volcanic breccia
64	2.5	cobble	cobble conglomerate		
32	1.2	pebble	pebble conglomerate		
4	0.15			lapilli	lapilli tuff
2	0.08	granule	granule conglomerate	course-grained ash	course-grained tuff
1	0.04	v crs sand	very course grd		
0.5	0.02	crs sand	course grd (sandstone)		
0.25	0.01	med sand	medium grd		
0.125	0.005	fine sand	fine grained		
0.063	0.002	v fn sand	very fine grd	fine-grained ash	fine-grained tuff
		silt	siltstone		
1/256	0.00015	clay	claystone or shale		

Fig. 6–9. Wentworth's (1922) particle-size classification.

SEDIMENTARY ROCKS

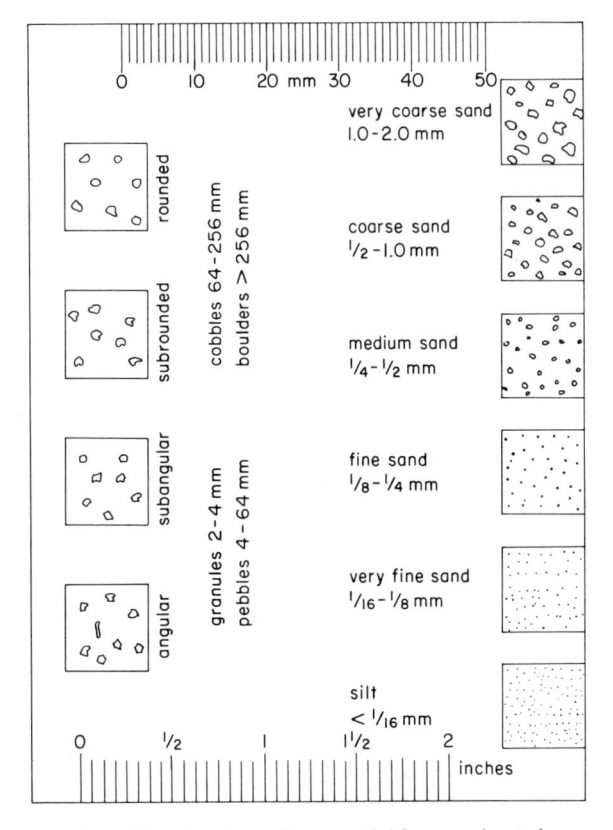

Fig. 6–10. Sketch of sand-gauge folder; a chart for comparison of grain size.

(for example, Krumbein and Sloss, 1959, page 81) for estimating roundness, as well as sphericity of grains, by visual comparison. Numerical values for each of the parameters have been assigned within a scale ranging from zero to one. Roundness also can be described in qualitative terms, such as angular, subangular, subrounded, rounded, and well-rounded. A useful classification of this kind, modified from Pettijohn (1957, page 52), is shown in Fig. 6–11.

Terms for describing shapes of grains include equant, spheroidal, discoidal, tabular, bladelike, and roller or prolate (rodlike). The relative lengths of the three principal dimensions of a particle lead to quantitative expressions of sphericity, with values ranging from nearly zero for a needlelike grain to one for a spherical grain.

Sorting of detrital grains is another feature of both

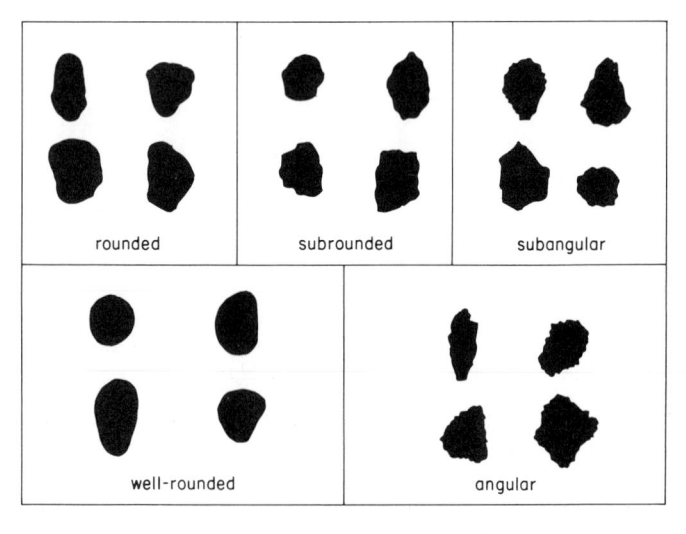

Fig. 6–11. Classification of roundness (modified from Pettijohn, 1957).

stratigraphic and genetic interest. A numerical index of sorting or a coefficient of sorting can be obtained in the laboratory by sieving the grains into fractions representing each of several ranges in size (Fig. 6–9), but only a visual estimate can be made in the field (by comparison with a sand gauge) to determine how closely the grains approach a single size.

If about three fourths of the grains are concentrated in several grain-size groups, for example within the fine to medium sand groups, the sand is well sorted (Payne, 1942). The sorting is fair if most of the grains are in four groups, and with any greater range of size, the sorting is poor. Some assemblages show a bimodal distribution in which many of the grains are in one size group, whereas many of the remainder are in another, quite different size group. For example, the majority of grains may be in the fine-grained sand size, but scattered throughout may be a considerable number of coarse-grained sand particles.

Grains commonly have a characteristic surface texture that can be recognized under the hand lens. Typical descriptive terms are dull, polished, striated, pitted, etched, and cupped. As these textures may be of genetic significance or of value in stratigraphic correlation, they should be noted in descriptions of a measured section.

Calciclastic and chemical rocks frequently are composed of interlocking aggregates of crystals, formed either by precipitation from saturated solutions (for example, rock salt, gypsum, anhydrite) or by recrystallization and dolomitization of materials such as calciclastic sands. Numerous classifications of crystal sizes have been suggested, most of which emphasize the very small sizes that require the use of a microscope. Payne's (1942, page 1706) classification, one that is often used, is as follows:

granular crystalline	2–4 mm	very finely crystalline	$1/16$–$1/8$ mm
very coarsely crystalline	1–2 mm	sublithographic	$1/256$–$1/16$ mm
coarsely crystalline	$1/2$–1 mm	lithographic	0.001–$1/256$ mm
medium crystalline	$1/4$–$1/2$ mm	cryptocrystalline	< 0.001 mm
finely crystalline	$1/8$–$1/4$ mm		

Any recrystallization or "metamorphic" textures should be noted; typical examples are coarsely crystalline replacement masses of dolomite in limestone, and large crystals of gypsum or pyrite in shale.

Cement and Porosity

The most common cementing materials of clastic rocks are quartz, calcite, (micrite and spar), dolomite, siderite, iron oxides, and clays. Depending upon the nature and amount of original cement as well as on the amount of subsequent leaching, the clastic rocks range from well-cemented and hard to poorly cemented and friable.

In siliciclastic rocks porosity, the percentage of void space in a rock or sediment, is related to cementation in that cements fill the pore space and eliminate porosity. Porosity in carbonate rocks may be primary, secondary, or related to dolomitization (Murray, 1960, page 61). Permeability is the amount of connected pore space through which fluids can move. In the field, the percentage porosity can be estimated on a freshly broken surface of the rock, or qualitative terms such as very porous, porous, slightly porous, and nonporous (Maher, 1959, page 28) can be applied. Other useful descriptive terms include cavernous, tubular, vuggy, pin-point, intergranular, intragranular, and intercrystal porosity. If possible, the origin and shape of the voids should be noted when deducing porosity of carbonate rocks.

Bedding

The dominant primary structure of most layered rocks is bedding or stratification. Each bed or stratum has some lithologic or structural unity caused by similar texture, color, or composition. Each may be a sedimentation unit, defined by Otto (1938) as "that thickness of sediment which was deposited under essentially constant physical conditions." But as noted by Pettijohn (1957), a sedimentary agent such as current flow is never absolutely uniform; hence for each sedimentation unit there is some average current that deposits, for example, some prevailing size of sediments.

Payne (1942) and McKee and Weir (1953) attempted to differentiate *stratum* and *lamination,* arbitrarily setting the dividing line between the two terms at one centimeter, a lamination being less than one centimeter thick. Otto (1938) and Pettijohn (1957), however, have considered laminations or laminae as internal parts of a sedimentation unit regardless of their thickness. For example, a cross-laminated bed of sandstone is a sedimentation unit with the cross laminae the result of short fluctuations in current velocity.

As summarized by Kelley (1956), many classifications include dimensional limits for terms such as *thin bedded* and *medium bedded,* but there is no general agreement on what these limits should be. The geologist may define his own thickness terminology for purposes of a particular project (Kottlowski *et al.*, 1956). More precise information is given by listing the actual thickness measured and by drawing graphic sketches that show thickness of the beds and their irregularity or evenness. In addition the beds should be described as continuous or tabular, wedgelike, lenticular, podlike, or irregular.

Structures of Sedimentary Rocks

Structures of sedimentary rocks are of three types: (1) those grossly related to bedding, (2) those on the bedding surfaces, and (3) chemical or secondary structures.

Those structures related to bedding include laminae, cross laminations, and graded bedding. Laminations or laminae, the thinnest units within beds, are found chiefly in the finer-grained sediments as alternations of calcite and silt-size quartz, as alternations of light- and dark-colored sediments (Fig. 6–12), and as alternations of fine-grained and coarser-grained layers. Contrasting laminae occur, for example, in varved lacustrine sediments characterized by lighter-colored summer layers of silt and sand alternating with darker-colored winter layers of silt and clay (Jahns and Willard, 1942, Plate 3B).

Cross laminations lie at an angle, normally 30° or less, to the bounding surfaces of stratification. Commonly they are either concave upward or are essentially planar. As cross laminations reflect the nature and direction of the currents responsible for their development, their thickness and orientation should be measured and recorded.

Typical graded beds occur in turbidites, the deposits of turbidity currents (Kuenen, 1950, page 366; Bouma,

Fig. 6–12. Light- and dark-colored laminae in gypsum beds.

1962; Menard, 1964, pages 214–218), varved lake sediments, some outwash and delta deposits, some ash falls, and many other similar detrital sediments. They are marked by gradations in grain size, from coarse to fine as traced from bottom to top of each bed, and are the result of gravity settling and associated hydrologic factors. The fine-grained material settles slowest mainly because of its small size.

Sedimentary structures on bedding planes include ripple marks, flute casts, groove casts, animal tracks and trails, rain prints, swash and rill marks, and desiccation cracks. Flute casts and groove casts were formed by turbidity currents and are elongated in the direction of the current (Potter and Pettijohn, 1963, pages 114–142). Ripple marks are of two types: (1) oscillation ripple marks, symmetric low ridges and hollows developed by the orbital motion of waves, generally aligned at right angles to wave direction, and (2) current ripple marks, asymmetric, with their relatively steep slope in the down-current direction.

Clay galls, shale flakes, clay shavings, and armored mud balls (balls of clay covered by small-size gravel) record contemporaneous channeling and erosion of clay beds, and are especially numerous in the basal part of heavy sands. They are commonly related to desiccation features.

Sedimentary features ascribable to chemical action include nodules, concretions, some veins, geodes, septaria, cone-in-cone, and regular crystal growths such as rosettes of gypsum and sand crystals. These structures may be usable in stratigraphic correlation, and thus they should be recorded and described. For example, items noted in describing concretions are their form, size, color, composition, internal structure, boundary against enclosing rock, relation to bedding, and distribution in the rock unit.

Weathered Surfaces

Weathering features, especially color and surface texture, are useful in many sections as a means for identification of specific units or layers. The color of a weathered rock surface can be identified precisely by comparison with a color chart or it can be named by inspection in terms of common color designations. In many situations, this color is different than the color of the freshly broken surface of the rock.

Weathering tends to emphasize minor differences in lithology and composition that may be overlooked in freshly broken rocks; thus the weathered surface may have striking characteristics not seen on fresh fractures of rocks that apparently are lithologically similar. For example, quartz grains stand up like beads on the weathered surface of some arenaceous calcarenites, whereas on others the quartz grains drop off and leave small pits. Typical descriptive terms applied to weathered surfaces are smooth, pitted, cupped, ribbed, laminated, reticulate-ribbed, grooved, and rough.

Topographic Expression

The gross and detailed topographic expression of layers is variously related to the inherent physical characteristics of the rocks, to the kinds of weathering processes involved, and to the geomorphic history of the area. Thick, hard, resistant layers, such as well-cemented sandstones in humid regions or sandstones and massive limestones in arid regions, commonly are useful marker beds for areal geologic mapping, structural studies, and correlation of sections. Differences in topographic expression throughout an area, and especially between measured sections, may provide clues to gradual or abrupt changes in lithology that otherwise are not apparent; for example, a lateral change from an argillaceous limestone into a calcareous shale may well be marked by a gradation from outcropping ledges to rubbly slopes.

Terms describing kinds of topographic expression include cliffs, ledges, or benches; rounded, vertical, or discontinuous; and slopes, lenticular, concave, convex, gullied, regular, or irregular. The quality of the exposures can be recorded by means of terms such as complete, good, fair, poor, or covered. As noted earlier, the description of a measured section should be accompanied by a sketched section showing either a profile of the outcrops (Fig. 6–5) or a vertical column with the topographic expression indicated along one side (Figs. 3–7 and 3–15).

Fossils

Fossils in sedimentary or metasedimentary rocks can be described as rock components, as indicators of environment—documents of milieu, as Pettijohn (1957) called them—and as means for correlation and age determination.

When fossils are described as typical clastic fragments, size, rounding due to abrasion, concentration in certain laminae or beds, leaching, recrystallization, and preservation as molds, casts, or carbon films are typical features to be noted. Observations on environment include arrangement, orientation, breakage, erosive effects, growth form, size, abundance, distribution, and sorting of the fossils. Factors for correlation are identification, to the full extent this is possible in the field, and association and abundance. So much work has been done and is in progress on the morphology and taxonomy of various fossils that any exact and up-to-date identification generally is made by specialists who are studying the different phyla. Thus the investigator ordinarily collects the fossils from the outcrop and sends them to the paleontologists who are most familar with the phyla represented.

Relations to Adjacent Units

Contacts between two measured units can be sharp or gradational, even or irregular, parallel or convergent # SEDIMENTARY ROCKS

with adjacent contacts, and exposed or covered. They may represent small changes in the nature of the deposition, large or small changes following an interval of no deposition, or changes following an interval of erosion. Some are cut-and-fill surfaces that do not mark any great depositional change or hiatus in time. Lateral tracing is often necessary to determine the areal relations of adjacent units and to interpret the significance of the boundary surface between them.

An unconformity is a contact surface between two rock units that represents an interval, commonly of long duration, during which either no sediments were deposited or some of the rocks were eroded and removed. Criteria for the recognition of unconformities, as suggested by Weller (1960, pages 383–413) and others, include: (1) evidence of erosion, such as angular discordance of beds above and below the erosional surface, cut-and-fill features, topographic irregularity beneath the unconformity, and coarse-grained siliciclastic beds overlying other types of rocks, (2) evidence of weathering, such as fossil soils, lag gravels, caliche beds, silicification, solution features, and conglomerates composed of resistant rock types from the underlying sequences, and (3) evidence of a hiatus, such as a gap in the fossil record where a faunal zone (or zones) is missing between two adjacent fossiliferous layers, or the absence of a lithologically distinctive unit that is present nearby.

Thickness of Measured Units

Thickness of the measured units is one of the principal descriptive features recorded, whether it is measured directly in the field or calculated later. Features noted along with the measurements, or as part of the measuring procedure, are strikes and dips, the surveying parameters that are needed, and lateral variations in thickness of the units. If the measured section is to have application beyond the locality in which it was measured, some notion concerning lateral variation or constancy must be obtained.

Sampling and Labeling

Many schemes have been devised for designating measured units and samples of all types of rocks, whether sedimentary, igneous, or metamorphic. As the location of the entire measured section should be indicated on a map and described adequately in field notes, the rock units can be identified simply by means of key letters and sequential numbers. For example, a section measured in Santa Ana Canyon can be designated SAC, with each contained unit given its proper number; starting from the base of the section, the units could be easily noted as SAC–1, SAC–2, and so on. Samples collected from the section should be labeled according to their source units, as RS–SAC–34 for a rock sample, FS–SAC–39 for a fossil. If more than one sample is collected from a single unit, they can be labeled RS–SAC–12a, RS–SAC–12b, RS–SAC–12c, and so on as required.

As noted in Chapter 1, samples are collected for various purposes; accordingly the method of sampling necessarily varies. If fresh chips are collected systematically throughout a measured unit in order to obtain a composite average sample for subsurface correlation, microfossils, or sediment studies, they can be placed together and labeled as a single sample. Alternatively, a representative sample of freshly broken rock, about 1 × 3 × 4 inches in size, may be taken from each rock type within a unit; such samples may be placed together or kept separately according to their intended use. When sampling rocks that may be of commercial value, large channel samples, cut vertically through the units, may be required (Peale and Church, 1941). Detailed specifications, such as those set up by the U.S. Bureau of Mines (Jackson and Knaebel, 1932), may need to be fulfilled. Each piece or each group of chips should be labeled in the field and securely tied in a labeled sample bag.

All samples collected should be marked with an "up" arrow. Oriented specimens should be marked with a north arrow and the directions of strike and dip, so that their original orientation can be reestablished at any time. Detailed description of the oriented specimen's outcrop relations must be recorded, and a sketch showing these relations should be drawn in the field notebook.

LAYERED IGNEOUS ROCKS

Layered igneous rocks can be measured stratigraphically in the same general manner as sedimentary rocks. Many volcanic rocks, including volcanic conglomerates, mudflows, ash flows, tuffaceous sandstones, and bentonites, are essentially sedimentary beds. Most volcanic rock units have a crude sheetlike distribution, even the extremely limited and lenticular vent agglomerates, as do the layered intrusive igneous rocks such as composite and differentiated dikes and sills.

Volcanic rocks range from being extremely variable over short distances to monotonously uniform throughout thick units. The geologist typically makes a reconnaissance of the area of volcanic rocks, then starts directly to map gross rock units. Observations of lithology, mineralogy, thickness, and their variations are made at every pertinent point and compiled into a composite description of the units. A description of the Bullion Canyon volcanics in central Utah (Willard and Callaghan, 1962), for example, provides information on the following features: type locality, area of occurrence, general stratigraphic succession, approximate thickness of the formation, and details of lithology, thickness, and petrography (including chemical and modal analyses) for local areas and for various parts of the sequence.

As most volcanic rocks are irregular and somewhat unpredictable, they cannot be well defined by measuring and describing isolated sections; extensive lateral tracing and areal mapping ordinarily are necessary to relate each part of a sequence to adjoining units. Layered intrusive igneous rocks may be more uniform, but lateral tracing is recommended.

Descriptive items noted for sedimentary rocks that also apply in part to igneous rocks include color, weathering surfaces, topographic expression, contact relations, and sampling and labeling. A schedule for describing layered igneous rocks such as flows, tuffs, and composite sills should include:

1. color, both fresh and weathered
2. texture
3. mineral composition
4. rock name
5. structures

6. inclusions
7. weathering features
8. shape of the unit
9. relations to adjacent rocks
10. thickness of the unit, including lateral variations
11. interpretation as to mode of emplacement if an intrusive rock, or type of accumulation if an extrusive igneous rock

The rock color is normally a composite of the colors of the constituent minerals or of the visible minerals and the enclosing matrix. The colors both on freshly broken and on weathered surfaces should be recorded. Nonclastic volcanic rocks rarely are coarsely crystalline; most are glassy, aphanitic, fine crystalline, or porphyritic with a fine crystalline, glassy, or aphanitic matrix. Typical crystal size categories are fine crystalline, less than 1 mm in diameter, medium crystalline, 1–5 mm, and coarse crystalline, greater than 5 mm. The visible minerals should be briefly described as to color, size, degree of crystallization (euhedral, subhedral, anhedral), crystal shape, cleavage, and relative abundance. The mineral composition and texture should suffice for assigning a provisional field name to the rock.

Structures of volcanic rocks can be designated by terms such as vesicular, amygdaloidal, ropy pahoehoe lava, blocky aa lava, pillows, flow banding, flow lines, spherulites, and so on. Layered intrusive rocks may have platy or linear structures; these should be described and their attitudes measured. Inclusions or xenoliths should be identified as to rock type, and their size, shape, and degree of metamorphism. Other features include color and texture of weathered surfaces, topographic expression, and differential alteration of various minerals. Any evidence of baking of underlying and overlying rocks, contact metamorphism of adjacent rocks, and possible weathering of the rock unit prior to extrusion of the overlying rocks also should be recorded.

A common field classification of fine-grained igneous rocks, assuming that at least 25 percent of the rock consists of identifiable minerals, is based chiefly on the relative percentages of quartz, potash feldspar, and plagioclase feldspar as follows:

1. rocks with 5 percent or more quartz
    a. potash feldspars dominant—rhyolite
    b. potash and plagioclase feldspars about equal—quartz latite
    c. plagioclase feldspars dominant—dacite
2. rocks with less than 5 percent quartz
    a. potash feldspars dominant—trachyte
    b. potash and plagioclase feldspars about equal—latite
    c. plagioclase feldspars dominant—andesite
    d. essentially no potash feldspars; plagioclase, augite, and/or olivine dominant—basalt

If feldspathoidal minerals such as nephelite, sodalite, and leucite are abundant, the rock may be called a phonolite or nephelite basalt. Obsidian, pitchstone, and perlite are types of glassy rocks, whereas a glassy porphyry is a vitrophyre.

Pyroclastic rocks are subdivided on the basis of grain size and grain composition. According to Wentworth and Williams (1932), ejected fragments more than 32 mm in diameter are called bombs if they were partly or wholly molten, or blocks if they were entirely solid when discharged. Clasts 4 mm to 32 mm across are called lapilli, ¼ mm to 4 mm coarse-grained ash, and those smaller than ¼ mm fine-grained ash. Lithified ash is called tuff, lithified bombs and matrix form agglomerate, and a rock composed mostly of blocks is termed volcanic breccia. If blocks are scattered amid a tuff matrix, the rock is called a tuff breccia.

Pyroclastic rocks rich in lapilli are lapilli tuffs. If the ash consists mainly of rock fragments, the corresponding rock is a lithic tuff, if chiefly of crystals a crystal tuff, whereas if the ash is mainly of glass shards, the rock is called a vitric tuff. Accumulations of dark-colored glassy ejected lapilli and bombs of basic composition are known as cinders and scoria; those of acid and intermediate composition generally are light colored and are termed pumice if their texture is porous and spongy.

Glowing avalanches form ignimbrites, welded tuffs, or ash-flow tuffs (Ross and Smith, 1961), in many places very thick and with vertical changes in texture. They are marked by a delicate, streaky lamination, flattened glass shards, and transitions outward from the center of the flow into obvious pyroclastic material (Williams, Turner, and Gilbert, 1954).

As tuffs are porous and contain fine-grained clasts, glass, and easily weathered loose minerals, they alter quickly. Feldspars break down into clays, typically montmorillonite, and silica-rich ashes are silicified by chalcedony and hydrated silica-opal. Glassy rocks, such as perlite, may be altered by weathering or by hydrothermal solutions to montmorillonite, silica minerals, and zeolites

(Weber, 1957). Thus, when measuring sections, pre-Tertiary pyroclastic rocks may be difficult to distinguish from dense felsites or from sedimentary claystones and chert.

METAMORPHIC ROCKS

Stratigraphy is a basic tool in the study of metamorphic rocks, as pointed out by Billings (1950). Thus any thorough investigation of metamorphic rocks should include the measuring and describing of stratigraphic sections. These will involve structural complications and changes in minerals not often found in sedimentary rocks. A description should include comments on metamorphic structures and textures.

A check list for the field description of metamorphic rocks, modified by Richard H. Jahns from a U.S. Geological Survey list, is as follows:

1. form and field name of the rock units; shape, lenticularity, dimensions
2. color of the rock as a whole, fresh and weathered, and color of individual parts or particles
3. composition; describe identifiable minerals and their percentages; compositional banding, inclusions; lateral or vertical variations; concentrations of minerals
4. texture and structure; degree of crystallization and granularity; porphyroblasts and other textural irregularities; foliation such as gneissic, schistose, slaty; contortions of the compositional layers or foliation; relic textures and structures
5. contacts; structural relation to adjacent rock units
6. type of metamorphism; cataclastic, thermal, dynamothermal, hydrothermal, plutonic

The principal textural classes of metamorphic rocks that may be identified in the field are (Williams, Turner, and Gilbert, 1954) hornfels, slate, phyllite, schist, amphibolite, gneiss, granulite, marble, and cataclasite.

GRAPHIC PRESENTATION

A columnar section, emphasizing gross and detailed lithology and topographic expression, should be sketched as part of the field description during measurement of a stratigraphic section, as already noted. This visual summary of the section permits quick correlation with other measured sections and provides a check on possible errors, such as omission of some layers or repetition of others through nonrecognition of a concealed fault. Distinctive features not sketched can be added in abbreviated form (see Appendix Table 4) beside the sketched column.

Three types of field-sketched columnar sections are profile sections, as illustrated by Fig. 6–5, vertical columns as in Figs. 2–7, 3–7, 3–15, and 5–3, and vertical columns that are integral parts of the written description, as shown in Fig. 6–3. The first two types can be sketched, either to scale or not, on the back of the preceding page in a field notebook or on the left side of the page, so that when the notebook is opened the columnar section appears either above or on the left of the written description.

For both informal and published reports, several types of graphic columns can be drawn after the field work is completed. Each measured section can be drafted carefully on a separate sheet (Fig. 6–13), showing the thick-

216

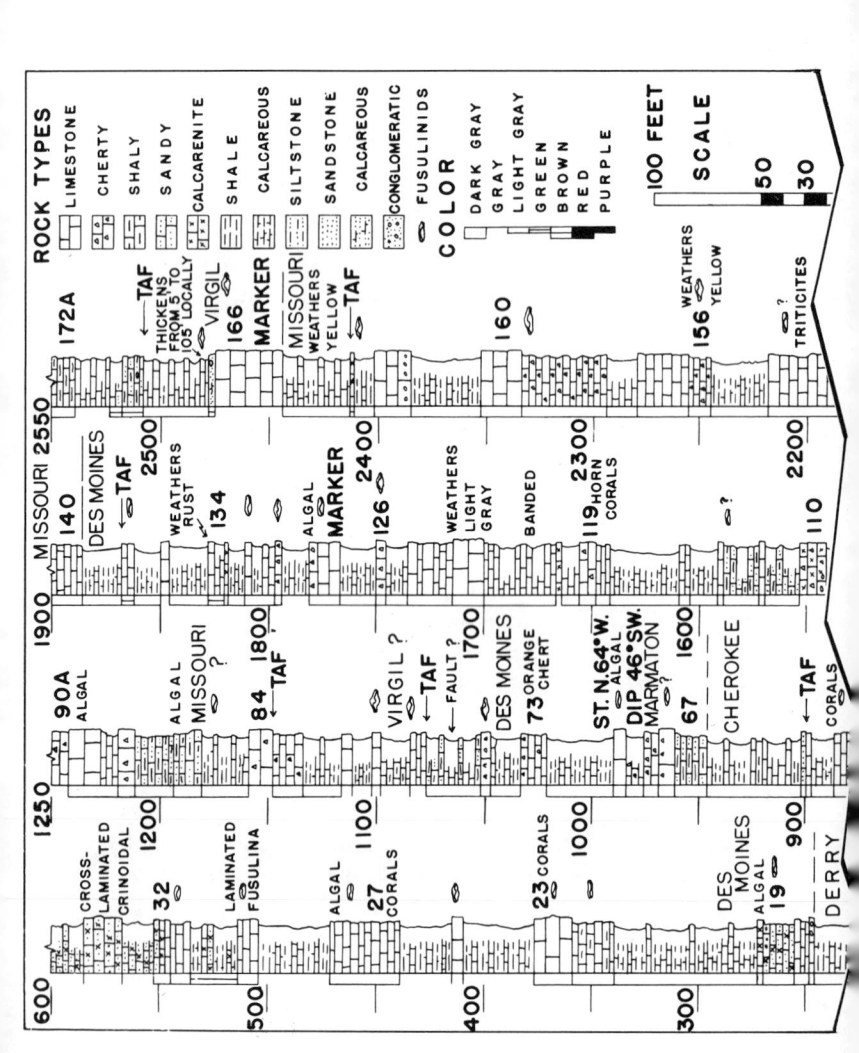

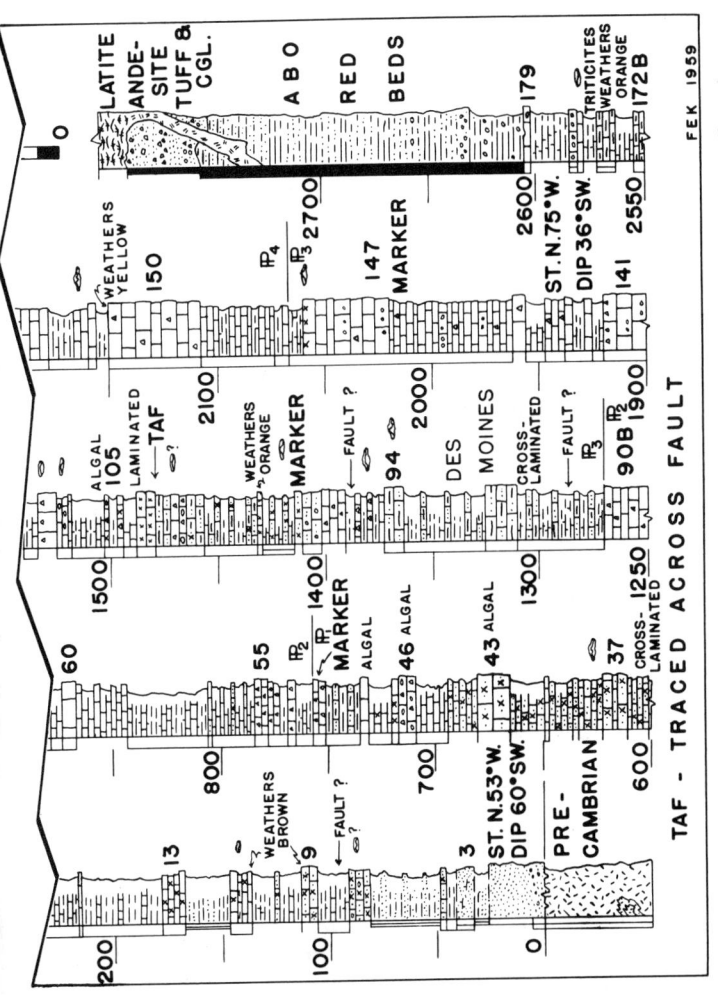

Fig. 6-13. Columnar section of Pennsylvanian rocks near Eaton Ranch, southwestern New Mexico.

ness of units, color, rock type, topographic expression, fossils and other distinctive features, unit numbers, formation names, ages, averaged strikes and dips, faults, and any other pertinent information.

If the measured section is thick, or if it is considered necessary to show the rock units in great detail, the columnar section at any readable scale will not fit on an 8½ × 11 inch sheet. A choice then lies between breaking the column into parallel segments on a single regular sheet (Fig. 6–13), or using a piece of drafting paper large enough to accommodate the full length of the column— even if the illustration reaches an unwieldy size such as 38 × 48 inches (Kottlowski *et al.*, 1956, Plate 1).

Normally more than one section is measured for a project involving stratigraphic studies. To illustrate correlations from one section to another throughout the area investigated, four types of columnar-section correlation diagrams can be drawn: (1) a skeleton cross section along a single line (Fig. 1–7), showing the various individual columnar sections with correlation lines drawn from one column to the next, (2) a diagrammatic cross section (Fig. 1–3) illustrating the rocks in the columnar sections and their probable distribution between these columns, (3) a fence or panel diagram comprising intersecting diagrammatic cross sections, and (4) a ribbon diagram (Weller, 1960, Fig. 271), which is a diagrammatic cross section that flows in graceful curves between various measured sections plotted in accordance with their actual locations.

Numerous "standard" lists of lithologic symbols are available in various text books, as well as being published by the American Association of Petroleum Geologist (Maher and Lukert, 1955), and by the U.S. Geological

Survey (Ridgway, 1920). More detailed lists are used by the various petroleum log companies, such as the American Stratigraphic Company of Denver. Suggested symbols that are useful for both rapid field sketching and finished illustrations are shown in Fig. 6–14. As there is considerable variance in the lithologic symbols applied by different geologists, the symbols used for a columnar section should be listed in a legend on the drawing (Fig. 6–13) or put in one "master legend" to serve several drawings.

FINAL PRESENTATION

A summary report on a measured section always should be prepared, even if it consists of only a few written pages or just a page to be placed in the files. This informal report should include any information compiled prior to the field work (for example, review of geologic literature, list of available maps and photographs), location of the section shown on an index map, a unit-by-unit description of the measured section expanded from field notes and from results of laboratory studies of the rocks and fossils, and a columnar section illustrating the principal features of the sequence. Such a report makes available the stratigraphic information for one's own later use in preparing a final report, for similar use by other geologists, and for correlation by other geologists with other measured sections.

Even an informal report should be illustrated by maps and columnar sections, and where necessary, by photographs of key outcrops. It should be typed if possible. If a standard transparent form is used (Fig. 6–15), the lithic description can be typed and duplicate copies

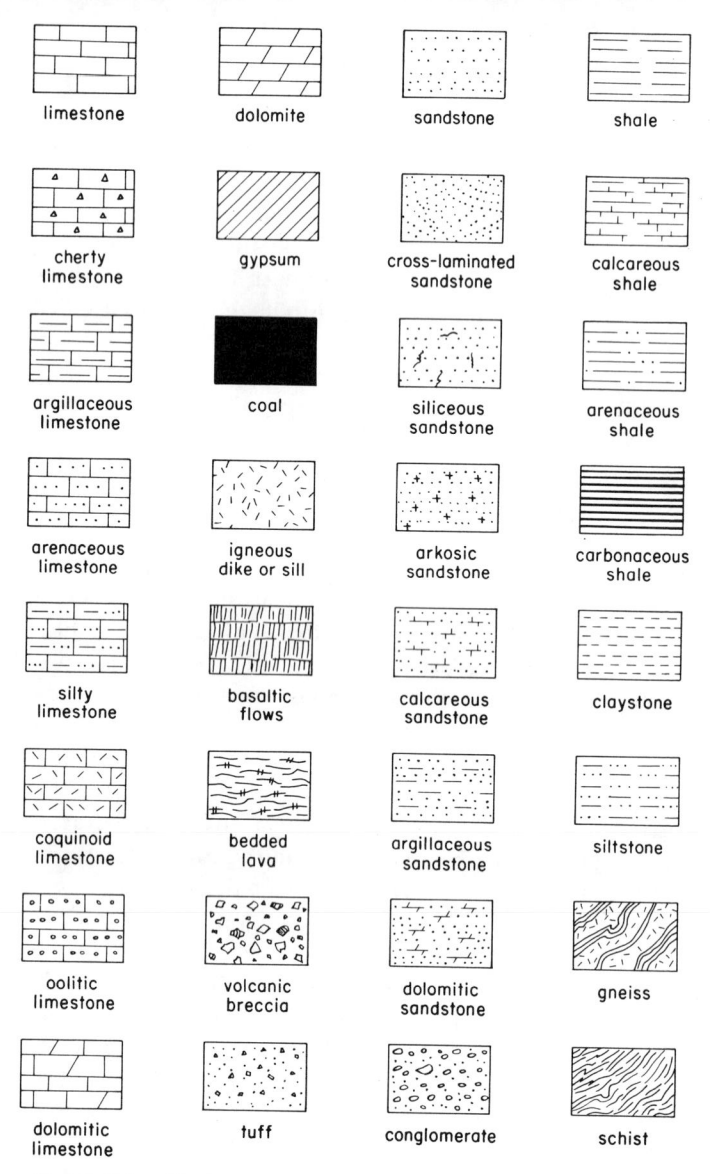

Fig. 6–14. Typical lithologic symbols for columnar sections.

Page no. 1
Quad no. 370 NW
Released by:

DESCRIPTION OF
MEASURED STRATIGRAPHIC SECTION

County: __Sierra__   Quadrangle: __Black Top Mtn. NW__   __Confidential__

Date measured: __7/7-9 & 9/30/54__   Section no.: __35-36 / 2-1__   Location of line of section

Name of section: __GA - Rhodes Canyon__

Measured by: __F. Kottlowski and R. Foster__

Agency or company: __N. M. Bureau of Mines__

Stratigraphic range: __Bursum (?) and lower Hueco__

formations, Wolfcampian

Township __13S__   Range __2E__

Section begins at: __Base Bursum cliff, 3750' N. of Rhodes Spring__

Section ends at: __In creek bed, 1750' NNE of Red House Spring__

Method of measurement: __Abney hand level and tape__

Remarks: __San Andres Mountains Project. Section described from base to top.__

Unit no.	Description	Thickness of unit in feet	of base
	BURSUM FORMATION (upper part)		
GA1	Limestone, medium light-gray, fine to coarse-crystalline, somewhat porous; crystals anhedral to subhedral, average 1 mm.; many tiny fossil fragments, scattered fossils; one massive cliff with units GA2-12; wavy indistinct bedding 2-4 feet apart; weathers medium-gray to light-gray; pitted and pointed (equivalent to G190)	5	5
GA2	Limestone, medium-gray to dark-gray; interbedded lenses of aphanitic to fine-crystalline limestone with medium to coarse-crystalline limestone; part of massive cliff	5	10

Fig. 6–15. Form for description of measured stratigraphic section.

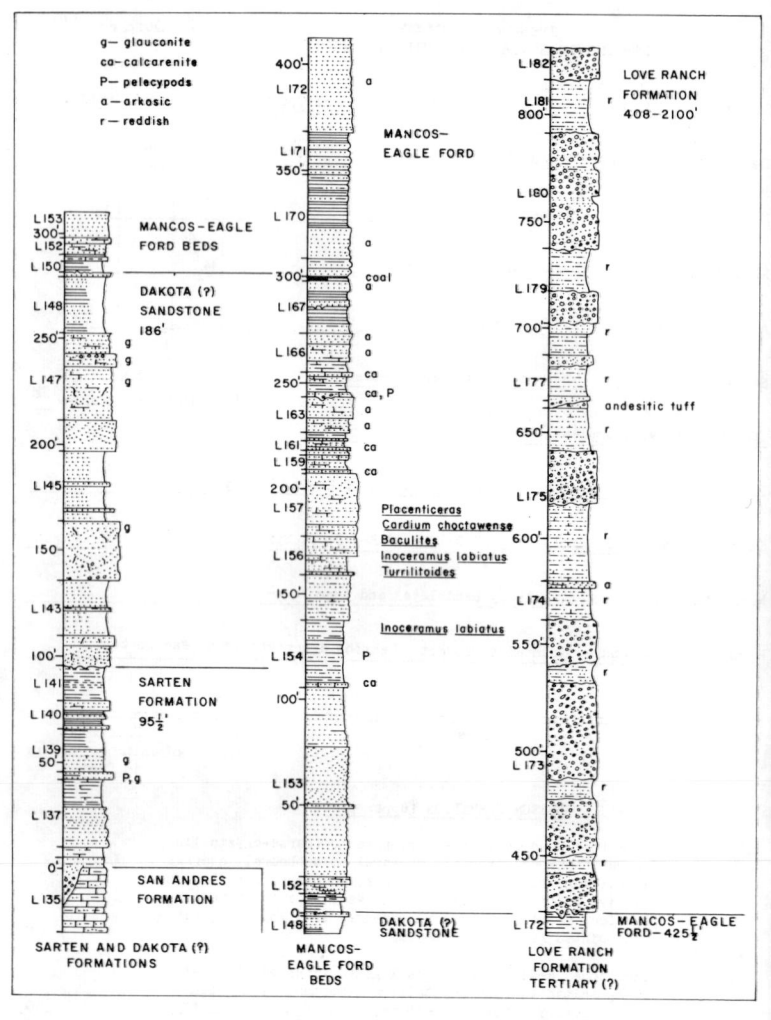

Fig. 6–16. Columnar section of Cretaceous and early Tertiary rocks in southern San Andres Mountains, New Mexico.

(Ozalid, Xerox, Thermofax) can be made at any later time without difficulty.

Published descriptions of measured stratigraphic sections constitute major parts of articles and reports on stratigraphy, subsurface correlation, areal geology, sedimentation studies, and paleontology. Necessary items are: (1) an index map, (2) a summary unit-by-unit description of the measured section, (3) a columnar section or group of columnar sections (Fig. 6–16), and (4) a summary description, in the text of the article or report, of the major features of the formations. Of additional value are photographs of outcrops or of rock samples and thin sections, as well as correlation diagrams and charts. In general descriptions of formations, the chief topics should include lithology, areal distribution, thickness, origin, stratigraphic relations, age (fossil lists), and correlations. The geologic features observed while measuring and describing the stratigraphic section are combined with interpretative comments for final presentation of the results.

Appendix

Table 1

Correction of Eye-Height Measurements for Dip
(eh × Cos Dip Angle)

Degrees of Dip	5.0	5.2	5.4	5.6	5.8	6.0	6.2
				Eye Heights			
2	5.0	5.2	5.4	5.6	5.8	6.0	6.2
4	5.0	5.2	5.4	5.6	5.8	6.0	6.2
6	5.0	5.2	5.4	5.6	5.8	6.0	6.2
8	4.9	5.1	5.3	5.5	5.7	5.9	6.1
10	4.9	5.1	5.3	5.5	5.7	5.9	6.1
12	4.9	5.1	5.3	5.5	5.7	5.9	6.1
14	4.9	5.0	5.2	5.4	5.6	5.8	6.0
16	4.8	5.0	5.2	5.4	5.6	5.8	6.0
18	4.8	4.9	5.1	5.3	5.5	5.7	5.9
20	4.7	4.9	5.1	5.3	5.5	5.6	5.8
22	4.6	4.8	5.0	5.2	5.4	5.6	5.7
24	4.6	4.8	4.9	5.1	5.3	5.5	5.7
26	4.5	4.7	4.9	5.0	5.2	5.4	5.6
28	4.4	4.6	4.8	4.9	5.1	5.3	5.5
30	4.3	4.5	4.7	4.8	5.0	5.2	5.4
32	4.2	4.4	4.6	4.7	4.9	5.1	5.3
34	4.1	4.3	4.5	4.6	4.8	5.0	5.1
36	4.0	4.2	4.4	4.5	4.7	4.9	5.0
38	3.9	4.1	4.3	4.4	4.6	4.7	4.9
40	3.8	4.0	4.1	4.3	4.4	4.6	4.7
42	3.7	3.9	4.0	4.2	4.3	4.5	4.6

Degrees of Dip	\multicolumn{7}{c}{Eye Heights}
	5.0	5.2	5.4	5.6	5.8	6.0	6.2
44	3.6	3.7	3.9	4.0	4.2	4.3	4.5
46	3.5	3.6	3.8	3.9	4.0	4.2	4.3
48	3.3	3.5	3.6	3.7	3.9	4.0	4.1
50	3.2	3.3	3.5	3.6	3.7	3.9	4.0

Table 2

**Stratigraphic Thickness from Dip and
Horizontal Distance Measured Normal to Strike**
($T = H$ Sin Dip Angle)

Degrees of Dip	100	200	300	400	500	600	700	800	900	1000
			Horizontal Distance in Feet							
2	3	7	10	14	17	21	24	28	31	35
4	7	14	21	28	35	42	49	56	63	70
6	10	21	31	42	52	63	73	84	94	105
8	14	28	42	56	70	83	97	111	125	139
10	17	35	52	69	87	104	122	139	156	174
12	21	42	62	83	104	125	145	166	187	208
14	24	48	73	97	121	145	169	193	218	242
16	28	55	83	110	138	165	193	220	248	276
18	31	62	93	124	155	186	216	247	278	309
20	34	68	103	137	172	206	240	274	308	342
22	37	75	112	150	187	225	262	300	337	375
24	41	81	122	163	204	245	286	326	367	407
26	44	88	131	175	219	263	307	351	395	438
28	47	94	141	188	235	282	329	375	423	469
30	50	100	150	200	250	300	350	400	450	500
32	53	106	159	212	265	318	371	424	477	530
34	56	112	168	224	280	336	391	447	503	559
36	59	118	176	236	294	353	412	471	529	588
38	62	123	185	246	308	370	431	492	554	616
40	64	129	193	257	322	386	450	514	579	643
42	67	134	201	268	334	402	468	535	602	669
44	69	139	209	278	348	417	486	556	625	695
46	72	144	215	288	359	431	503	575	647	719
48	74	149	223	298	372	446	520	594	668	743
50	77	153	230	307	383	460	537	613	690	766

Table 3

Natural Sines, Cosines, Tangents, and Cotangents

Degrees	Sine	Cosine	Tangent	Cotangent	Degrees
0	.000	1.0	.000	Infinity	0
1	.017	1.0	.017	57.290	1
2	.035	.999	.035	28.636	2
3	.052	.999	.052	19.081	3
4	.070	.998	.070	14.301	4
5	.087	.996	.087	11.430	5
6	.105	.995	.105	9.514	6
7	.122	.993	.123	8.144	7
8	.139	.990	.141	7.115	8
9	.156	.988	.158	6.314	9
10	.174	.985	.176	5.671	10
11	.191	.982	.194	5.145	11
12	.208	.978	.212	4.705	12
13	.225	.974	.231	4.331	13
14	.242	.970	.249	4.011	14
15	.259	.966	.268	3.732	15
16	.276	.961	.287	3.487	16
17	.292	.956	.306	3.271	17
18	.309	.951	.325	3.078	18
19	.326	.946	.344	2.904	19
20	.342	.940	.364	2.747	20
21	.358	.934	.384	2.605	21
22	.375	.927	.404	2.475	22

Degrees	Sine	Cosine	Tangent	Cotangent	Degrees
23	.391	.920	.424	2.356	23
24	.407	.914	.445	2.246	24
25	.423	.906	.466	2.145	25
26	.438	.899	.488	2.050	26
27	.454	.891	.510	1.963	27
28	.469	.883	.532	1.881	28
29	.485	.875	.554	1.804	29
30	.500	.866	.577	1.732	30
31	.515	.857	.601	1.664	31
32	.530	.848	.625	1.600	32
33	.545	.839	.649	1.540	33
34	.559	.829	.675	1.483	34
35	.574	.819	.700	1.428	35
36	.588	.809	.727	1.376	36
37	.602	.799	.754	1.327	37
38	.616	.788	.781	1.280	38
39	.629	.777	.810	1.235	39
40	.643	.766	.839	1.192	40
41	.656	.755	.869	1.150	41
42	.669	.743	.900	1.111	42
43	.682	.731	.933	1.072	43
44	.694	.719	.966	1.036	44
45	.707	.707	1.000	1.000	45

Table 4

Abbreviations for Descriptions of Measured Units

above	abv	brachiopod	Brac
abundant	abd	breccia	Brc
acicular	aci	brown	bn
agglomerate	Agl	bryozoa	Bry
algae, algal	Alg	calcite	Cal
altered	alt	calcareous	calc
angular	ang	carbonaceous	carb
andesite	An	cement	cmt
anhedral	anh	cephalopod	Cep
anhydrite	Ahy	chalcedony	Chal
aragonite	Arg	chert, cherty	ch
arenaceous	aren	claystone	Clst
argillaceous	arg	coarse	crs
arkose, arkosic	Ark	cobble	Cob
at this point	ATP	concretion	conc
average	av	conglomerate	Cgl
banded	bnd	conodont	Cono
basalt	Bas	contact	ctk
bed	bd	coquina	Coq
bedded	bdd	covered	cov
bentonite	Ben	crinoid	Crn
biotite	Bio	cross-bedded	xbd
bituminous	bitu	cross-bedding	xbg
black	bk	cross-laminated	xlam
boulder	Bld	crystal	xl

232

APPENDIX

crystalline	xln	granite	Gr
dacite	Dac	granodiorite	Grd
dark	dk	granular	gran
diabase	Db	graptolite	Grap
diameter	dia	gray	gy
diorite	Dio	graywacke	Gyw
disseminated	dism	green	grn
dolomite	Dol	gypsum, gypsiferous	Gyp
elevation	Elev	hard	hd
echinoid	Ech	hematite	Hem
elliptical	elip	hornblende	Hbd
euhedral	euh	igneous	ign
feldspar, feldspathic	feld	interbedded	inbd
ferruginous	Fe	intercalated	incl
fine	fn	interfingered	infg
fissile	fis	intraformational	infm
foliated	fol	iron	Fe
foraminifera	Foram	irregular	irg
formation	Fm	joints	jts
fossil, fossiliferous	fos	laminated	lam
fragment, fragmental	frag	large	lar
		latite	Lat
fresh fracture	ff	ledge	ldg
friable	fri	lenticular	len
frosted	frs	lignite	Lig
fusulinid	Fus	light	lt
gabbro	Gb	limestone	Ls
gastropod	Gst	limonite	Lim
glauconite	glau	little	ltl
glassy	gla	long	lg
gneiss	Gns	lower	low
grained	grd	magnetite	Mag

massive	mas	porous	por
matrix	mtx	porphyritic	ppy
medium	m	probable	prob
member	Mbr	prominent	prom
metamorphic	meta	purple	pur
mica, micaceous	Mic, mic	pyrite	Py
		quartz	Qtz
mollusca	Mol	quartzite	Qtzt
monzonite	Mnz	quartzose	qtse
mottled	mot	range, ranging	rng
mudstone	Mdst	rare	rr
muscovite	Musc	rhyolite	Rhy
nodule, nodular	nod	rocks	rk
olive	ol	rounded	rd
oolite, oolitic	ool	sample	spl
orthoclase	Orth	sand	Sd
ostracod	Ost	sandstone	Ss
outcrop	oc	sandy	sy
part, partly	pt	schist	Sch
pebble	Pbl	secondary	sec
pelecypod	Pcy	sedimentary	sed
pellet	pel	selenite	Sel
permeability	perm	shale	Sh
petroliferous	pet	shaly	shy
phenocryst	phen	siderite	Sid
phosphate, phosphatic	phos	siliceous	sil
pink	pk	silt	St
pin-point	pp	siltstone	Sts
pisolitic	piso	size	sz
pitted	pit	small	s
plagioclase	Plag	smooth	smo
plant	pl	soft	sft
		sort, sorted	srt

APPENDIX

speckled	spk	unconformity	unconf
spotted	spt	upper	up
stain, stained	stn	variable	var
stylolite	sty	variegated	vgt
subangular	sang	very	v
subhedral	sbh	vesicular	ves
subrounded	srd	volcanic	vol
sulfur	S	vug, vuggy	vug
tabular	tab	weather, weathered	wd
texture	tex		
thick	tk	well	w
thin	tn	white	wh
tight	tt	with	/ or wi
trilobite	Tri	yellow	yel
tuff	Tf	zone	zn

Table 5

Simple Trigonometric Relations

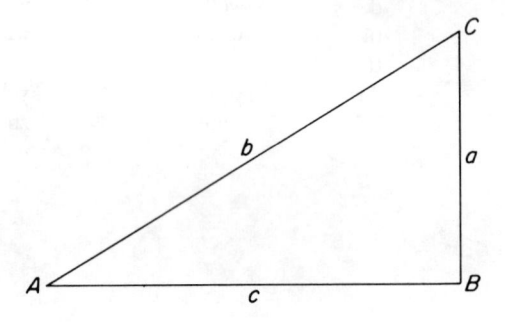

Fig. A1. Right triangle.

$$\sin A = \frac{a}{b} = \cos C \qquad \cos A = \frac{c}{b} = \sin C$$

$$\tan A = \frac{a}{c} = \cot C \qquad \cot A = \frac{c}{a} = \tan C$$

$$a = b \sin A = b \cos C = c \tan A = c \cot C$$

$$b = \frac{a}{\sin A} = \frac{a}{\cos C} = \frac{c}{\cos A} = \frac{c}{\sin C}$$

$$c = b \cos A = b \sin C = a \tan A = a \cot C$$

$$C = 90° - A \qquad b = \sqrt{a^2 + c^2} \qquad a = \sqrt{(b+c)(b-a)}$$

APPENDIX

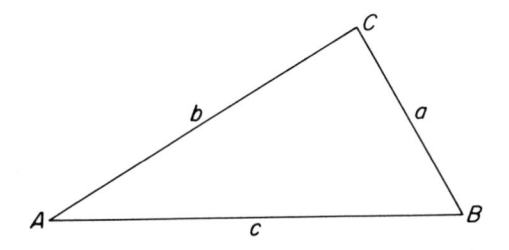

Fig. A2. Oblique triangle.

$$\frac{a}{\sin A} = \frac{b}{\sin B} = \frac{c}{\sin C} \qquad a = \frac{b \sin A}{\sin B} = \frac{c \sin A}{\sin C}$$

a, A, C known : $c = \dfrac{a \sin C}{\sin A} \qquad b = \dfrac{a \sin (A + C)}{\sin A}$

a, c, A known : $b = \dfrac{a \sin B}{\sin A} \qquad \sin C = \dfrac{c \sin A}{a}$

a, b, c known : $s = \tfrac{1}{2}(a + b + c) \qquad \cos \tfrac{1}{2} A = \sqrt{\dfrac{s(s-a)}{bc}}$

References Cited

American Commission on Stratigraphic Nomenclature, "Code of Stratigraphic Nomenclature," *Am. Assoc. Petroleum Geol. Bull.*, 1961, vol. 45, pp. 645–665.

Anderson, Charles G., "Stadia Tables for Obtaining Differences in Elevation," *U.S. Geol. Survey Admin. Publ.*, 1937, 26 pp.

Bergstrom, John R., "Jacob Staff—Refined," *Am. Assoc. Petroleum Geol. Bull.*, 1958, vol. 42, pp. 2251–2254.

Billings, Marland P., "Stratigraphy and the Study of Metamorphic Rocks," *Geol. Soc. Am. Bull.*, 1950, vol. 61, pp. 435–448.

———, *Structural Geology*. Englewood Cliffs, N.J.: Prentice-Hall, 1954.

Blackwelder, Eliot, "A Modification of the Walcott Method of Measuring Stratigraphic Sections," *Econ. Geol.*, 1913, vol. 8, pp. 489–492.

Bouma, Arnold H., *Sedimentology of Some Flysch Deposits*. Amsterdam: Elsevier, 1962.

Braunstein, Jules, "Calciclastic and Silciclastic," *Am. Assoc. Petroleum Geol. Bull.*, 1961, vol. 45, pp. 2017.

Broggi, Jorge A., " 'Jacob Staff' and Measurements of Stratigraphic Sequences," *Am. Assoc. Petroleum Geol. Bull.*, 1946, vol. 30, pp. 716–725 and 1934.

Bryant, Donald L., and McClymonds, Neal E., "Permian Concha Limestone and Rainvalley Formation, Southeastern Arizona," *Am. Assoc. Petroleum Geol. Bull.*, 1961, vol. 45, pp. 1324–1333.

REFERENCES CITED

Busk, H. G., *Earth Flexures.* Cambridge: Cambridge Univ. Press, 1929.

Capps, Stephen R., "An Ancient Volcanic Eruption in the Upper Yukon Basin," *U.S. Geol. Survey Profess. Paper* 95, 1915, p. 59–64.

Compton, Robert R., *Manual of Field Geology.* New York: Wiley, 1962.

Deiss, Charles F., "Cambrian Formations and Sections in Part of Cordilleran Trough," *Geol. Soc. Am. Bull.,* 1938, vol. 49, pp. 1067–1168.

———, "Stratigraphy and Structure of Southwest Saypo Quadrangle, Montana," *Geol. Soc. Am. Bull.,* 1943, vol. 54, pp. 205–262.

Dunham, Robert J., "Classification of Carbonate Rocks According to Depositional Texture," in "Classification of Carbonate Rocks," *Am. Assoc. Petroleum Geol.,* 1962, Mem. 1, pp. 108–121.

Folk, Robert L., "Practical Petrographic Classification of Limestones," *Am. Assoc. Petroleum Geol. Bull.,* 1959, vol. 43, pp. 1–38.

———, "Spectral Subdivision of Limestone Types," in "Classification of Carbonate Rocks," *Am. Assoc. Petroleum Geol.,* 1962, Mem. 1, pp. 62–84.

Forrester, James D., *Principles of Field and Mining Geology.* New York: Wiley, 1946.

Geikie, James, *Structural and Field Geology.* Princeton, N.J.: Van Nostrand, 1920.

Gilbert, Charles M., "Welded Tuff in Eastern California," *Geol. Soc. Am. Bull.,* 1938, vol. 49, pp. 1829–1862.

Gilliland, William N., "Graphical Use of Cotangent in Determining Dip or Components of Dip," *Am. Assoc. Petroleum Geol. Bull.,* 1954, vol. 38, pp. 160–161.

Gilluly, James, Cooper, John R., and Williams, James S., "Late Paleozoic Stratigraphy of Central Cochise County, Arizona," *U.S. Geol. Survey Profess. Paper* 266, 1954, 49 pp.

REFERENCES CITED

Goddard, Edwin N., et al., "Rock Color Chart," *Geol. Soc. Am.*, 1951, 11 pp.

Greenly, Edward, and Williams, Howel, *Methods in Geological Surveying*. Princeton, N.J.: Van Nostrand, 1930.

Ham, William E., "Classification of Carbonate Rocks, A Symposium," *Am. Assoc. Petroleum Geol.*, 1962, Mem. 1.

———, and Pray, Lloyd C., "Modern Concepts and Classifications of Carbonate Rocks," in "Classification of Carbonate Rocks," *Am. Assoc. Petroleum Geol.*, 1962, Mem. 1, pp. 2–19.

Hansen, Wallace R., "Improved Jacob Staff for Measuring Inclined Stratigraphic Intervals," *Am. Assoc. Petroleum Geol. Bull.*, 1960, vol. 44, pp. 252–254.

Hayes, Charles W., *Handbook for Field Geologists*. New York: Wiley, 1909.

Hewett, Donnel F., "Measurements of Folded Beds," *Econ. Geol.*, 1920, vol. 15, pp. 367–385.

Jackson, Charles F., and Knaebel, John B., "Sampling and Estimation of Ore Deposits," *U.S. Bur. Mines Bull.* 356, 1932.

Jahns, Richard H., and Willard, Max E., "Late Pleistocene and Recent Deposits in the Connecticut Valley, Massachusetts," *Am. J. Sci.*, 1942, vol. 240, pp. 161–191 and 265–287.

Kelley, Vincent C., "Thickness of Strata," *J. Sediment. Petrol.*, 1956, vol. 26, pp. 289–300.

Klein, George DeV., "Analysis and Review of Sandstone Classifications in the North American Geological Literature, 1940–1960," *Geol. Soc. Am. Bull.*, 1963, vol. 74, pp. 555–575.

Kottlowski, Frank E., "Summary of Pennsylvania Sections in Southwestern New Mexico and Southeastern Arizona," *New Mexico Inst. Mining and Technol., State Bur. Mines and Mineral Resources*, 1960, Bull. 66, 187 pp.

———, "Paleozoic and Mesozoic Strata of Southwestern and

South-Central New Mexico," *New Mexico Inst. Mining and Technol., State Bur. Mines and Mineral Resources,* 1963, Bull. 79, 100 pp.

———, Flower, Rousseau H., Thompson, M. Luther and Foster, Roy W., "Stratigraphic Studies of the San Andres Mountains, New Mexico," *New Mexico Inst. Mining and Technol., State Bur. Mines and Mineral Resources,* 1956, Mem. 1, 132 pp.

Krumbein, William C., and Sloss, Lawrence C., *Stratigraphy and Sedimentation.* San Francisco: W. H. Freeman, 1959.

Kuenen, Philip H., *Marine Geology.* New York: Wiley, 1950.

Kummel, Bernhard, Jr., "New Technique for Measurement of Stratigraphic Units," *Am. Assoc. Petroleum Geol. Bull.,* 1943, vol. 27, pp. 220–222.

Lahee, Frederic H., *Field Geology.* New York: McGraw-Hill, 1961.

Larsen, Esper S., Jr., and Cross, Whitman, "Geology and Petrology of the San Juan Region, Southwestern Colorado," *U.S. Geol. Survey Profess. Paper* 258, 1956, 303 pp.

Lattman, Laurence H., and Ray, Richard G., *Aerial Photographs in Field Geology.* New York: Holt, Rinehart and Winston, 1965.

Leighton, Morris W., and Pendexter, Charles, "Carbonate Rock Types," in "Classification of Carbonate Rocks," *Am. Assoc. Petroleum Geol.,* 1962, Mem. 1, pp. 33–61.

Low, Julian W., *Plane Table Mapping.* New York: Harper & Row, 1952.

———, *Geologic Field Methods.* New York: Harper & Row, 1957.

McKee, Edwin D., and Weir, Gordon W., "Terminology for Stratification and Cross-Stratification," *Geol. Soc. Am. Bull.,* 1953, vol. 64, pp. 381–390.

Maher, John C., "The Composite Interpretive Method of

REFERENCES CITED

Logging Drill Cuttings," *Oklahoma Geol. Survey,* 1959, Guidebook 8, 48 pp.

———, and Lukert, Louis H., "Suggestions for Preparation of Regional Stratigraphic Cross Sections," *Am. Assoc. Petroleum Geol. Bull.,* 1955, vol. 39, pp. 1655–1667.

Menard, Henry W., *Marine Geology of the Pacific.* New York: McGraw-Hill, 1964.

Mertie, John B., Jr., "Graphic and Mechanical Computation of Thickness of Strata and Distance to a Stratum," *U.S. Geol. Survey Profess. Paper* 129, 1922, pp. 39–52.

———, "Stratigraphic Measurements in Parallel Folds," *Geol. Soc. Am. Bull.,* 1940, vol. 51, pp. 1107–1134.

Murray, Richard C., "Origin of Porosity in Carbonate Rocks," *J. Sediment. Petrol.,* 1960, vol. 30, pp. 59–84.

Otto, George H., "The Sedimentation Unit and Its Use in Field Sampling," *J. Geol.,* 1938, vol. 46, pp. 569–582.

Palmer, Harold S., "New Graphic Method for Determining the Depth and Thickness of Strata and the Projection of Dip," *U.S. Geol. Survey Profess. Paper* 120, 1918, pp. 122–128.

Patton, John B., "Crushed Stone in Indiana," *Indiana Geol. Survey,* 1949, Rept. Prog. No. 3, 47 pp.

Payne, Thomas G., "Stratigraphical Analysis and Environmental Reconstruction," *Am. Assoc. Petroleum Geol. Bull.,* 1942, vol. 26, pp. 1697–1770.

Peele, Robert, and Church, John A., *Mining Engineers Handbook.* New York: Wiley, 1941.

Perry, Thomas G., Smith, Ned M., and Wayne, William J., "Salem Limestone and Associated Formations in South-Central Indiana," *Indiana Geol. Survey,* 1954, Field Conf. Guidebook No. 7, 73 pp.

Pettijohn, Francis J., *Sedimentary Rocks.* New York: Harper & Row, 1957.

Potter, Paul E., and Pettijohn, Francis J., *Paleocurrents and Basin Analysis.* New York: Academic Press, 1963.

Pray, Lloyd C., "Geology of the Sacramento Mountains Escarpment, Otero County, New Mexico," *New Mexico Inst. Mining and Technol., State Bur. Mines and Mineral Resources,* 1961, Bull. 35, 144 pp.

———, and Wray, John L., "Porous Algal Facies (Pennsylvanian), Honaker Trail, San Juan Canyon, Utah," in "Shelf Carbonates of the Paradox Basin," *Four Corners Geol. Soc.,* 1963, pp. 204–234.

Proctor, Paul D., "Field Geology for the Advanced Student," *J. Geol. Education,* 1961, vol. 9, pp. 39–46.

Ridgway, John L., "The Preparation of Illustrations," *U.S. Geol. Survey Admin. Publ.,* 1920, 101 pp.

Robinson, Gershon D., "Measuring Dipping Beds," GeoTimes, *Am. Geol. Inst.,* 1959, vol. 4, no. 1, pp. 8–9, 24–25, 27.

Ross, Clarence S., and Smith, R. L., "Ash-Flow Tuffs: Their Origin, Geologic Relations, and Identification," *U.S. Geol. Survey Profess. Paper* 366, 1961.

Satin, Lowell R., "Apparent-Dip Computer," *Geol. Soc. Am. Bull.,* 1960, vol. 71, pp. 231–234.

Shrock, Robert R., *Sequence in Layered Rocks.* New York: McGraw-Hill, 1948.

Thornbury, William D., *Principles of Geomorphology.* New York: Wiley, 1954.

Threet, Richard L., "Automatic Dip-Component Computer for Use with Brunton Compass," *Am. Assoc. Petroleum Geol. Bull.,* 1957, vol. 41, pp. 2752–2753.

———, "A Simplified Slide Rule for Stratigraphic Section Measurement," *J. Geol. Education,* 1961, vol. 9, pp. 70–73.

———, "Jacob Staff Paradox," *Geol. Soc. Am. Bull.,* 1962, vol. 73, pp. 1299–1301.

Twenhofel, William H., and Tyler, Stanley A., *Methods of Study of Sediments.* New York: McGraw-Hill, 1941.

Walcott, Charles D., "Measurement of Stratigraphic Sections," *U.S. Natl. Museum Proc.,* 1888, pp. 447–448.

REFERENCES CITED

Weber, Robert H., "Geology and Petrography of the Stendel Perlite Deposit, Socorro County, New Mexico," *New Mexico Inst. Mining and Technol., State Bur. Mines and Mineral Resources,* 1957, Circ. 44, 22 pp.

Weller, J. Marvin, *Stratigraphic Principles and Practice.* New York: Harper & Row, 1960.

Wengerd, Sherman A., *Laboratory Manual in Sedimentology.* Albuquerque: Dept. Geol., Univ. New Mexico, 1955.

Wentworth, Chester K., "A Scale of Grade and Class Terms for Clastic Sediments," *J. Geol.,* 1922, vol. 30, pp. 377–392.

———, and Williams, Howel, "The Classification and Terminology of the Pyroclastic Rocks," *Natl. Research Council,* 1932, Bull. 89, pp. 19–53.

Willard, Max E., "Sedimentology of the Upper Cretaceous Rocks of Todilto Park, New Mexico," *New Mexico Inst. Mining and Technol., State Bur. Mines and Mineral Resources,* 1963, Mem. 14, 47 pp.

———, and Callaghan, Eugene, "Geology of the Marysvale Quadrangle, Utah," *U.S. Geol. Survey,* 1962, Geol. Map. 154.

Williams, Howel, Turner, Francis J., and Gilbert, Charles M., *Petrography.* San Francisco: W. H. Freeman, 1954.

Wilpolt, Ralph H., *et al.,* "Geologic Map and Stratigraphic Sections of Paleozoic Rocks of Joyita Hills, Los Pinos Mountains, and Northern Chupadera Mesa, Valencia, Torrance, and Socorro Counties, New Mexico," *U.S. Geol. Survey,* 1946, Oil and Gas Prelim. Map No. 61.

Index

Index

Abbreviations, for lithic terms, 182, 215, 232–235

Abney hand level, to determine grade, 83
  errors in use, 172
  for eye-height measurements, 75, 85–88, 90
  as field equipment, 46, 52
  with Jacob staff, 61, 69, 71
  specific uses, 136, 137, 140
  for vertical angles, 95

Accuracy, defined, 170–171
  limitations, 46, 136
  of measurements, 2, 133, 138
  and speed, 56, 59

Aerial photographs, for checking thicknesses, 132, 137
  for horizontal distance, 81, 94
  in locating sections, 31–35, 45, 52–53
  measurements from, 122–127
  recording locations, 67, 219
  used in geologic mapping, 15–16, 144

Against-dip measuring, 72–74, 136, 152–153

Altimeter, with aerial photographs, 53, 132
  to determine elevations, 106
  for measuring sections, 125–129, 137, 167

American Association of Petroleum Geologists, 32, 218

American Commission on Stratigraphic Nomenclature, 16

Apparent-dip tables, 71, 91

Averaging strikes and dips, arc method, 160, 162–164
  by averaging bearings, 145, 147, 160
  by averaging dips, 161–162, 164
  by averaging distances, 145, 146, 160–163
  See also zigzag traverses

Beaman arc, 100–102, 105, 108

249

Bedding, cross bedding, 44
    defined, 201–202
    described, 4, 50–51, 56, 185, 187
    related to measuring, 59
Brunton compass, with altimeter, 127
    to determine grade, 83
    errors in use, 172
    for eye-height measurements, 78, 130, 140, 167
    as field equipment, 46, 52
    for Hewett method, 88–91, 126, 136, 137, 171
    with Jacob staff, 54, 61, 68–70, 75, 104
    to level plane table, 93
    with tape, 112–122, 124, 131, 136
    for vertical angles, 95, 125

Cement of sedimentary rocks, described, 189, 191, 200
    listing of, 185, 187, 194, 205
Check lists, for section description, 56, 181–185
Code, stratigraphic, 16
Color, of rocks, classified, 181, 193–195, 201–204, 211
    listed, 5, 50, 185, 210, 214, 218
    weathered, 7, 51, 54, 204
Color chart, 181, 195, 204
Columnar sections (graphic sections), with descriptions, 56, 67, 181–182, 185, 206
    illustrated, 8–9, 23, 29, 57, 69, 79–80, 178, 186, 188, 222
    with reports, 215–219, 223
    for stratigraphic studies, 4–6, 18–20
Compass-tape method, described, 112–119
    with other methods, 131–132
    uses, 68, 70, 121, 124, 131, 136–137, 140–141, 146, 148, 149, 151–154
Conglomerate, classification of, 189
Crystallinity, 187, 195, 199–200, 211, 214

Deiss, Charles F., 38
Drill cuttings, 7, 8, 21, 51, 67, 174

Engineering geology, 7
Erosion surfaces, 10, 11, 44, 207

Faults, errors due to, 174–178, 215
    in sections, 10, 24, 25, 31, 43, 55, 169, 218

INDEX

Fence diagrams, 21, 218
Fossils, collecting, 2, 18–20, 28, 47, 54–56, 67, 105–106, 114, 124
  described, 191, 206, 207
  listed, 1, 17, 50, 127, 185, 187, 208, 218–223
Foster, Roy W., 182, 184

Geologic map index, 33
Geologic mapping (*see* Mapping, geologic)
Geological Society of America, 32, 195
Grade, 81–85, 88
Gradienter drum, 102–103
Grain size, 28, 50, 187–190, 195–196, 199, 203
Graphic rock symbols, 219–220
Graphic sections (*see* Columnar sections)
Ground-water studies, 6–7

Hand-leveling, with Abney hand level, 85, 167
  with Brunton compass, 89–90
  described, 77–81
  with Jacob staff, 61
  with simple level, 65, 75, 84, 104, 130
  specific uses, 136–137, 140
Heavy minerals, 19, 21, 193

Hewett method, with Abney hand level, 85–87
  with Brunton compass, 88–91, 131–132, 136–138
  errors in, 168, 171
  uses of, 46, 133–134, 149, 151, 154, 165

Igneous rock classification, 212

Jacob staff, errors with, 171–172
  as field equipment, 46, 52–54, 87, 104
  measurements with, 61–75, 124
  with other methods, 100, 106, 120, 130–134, 165, 167
  specific uses, 78, 84, 119, 126, 136–138, 140, 149, 151–154, 160
Jahns, Richard H., 214

Key beds, 25, 43, 51, 53, 149, 174, 177, 179, 219

Limestone classification, 191–192
Lithic terms, abbreviations for, 182, 215, 232–235

Locke hand level, 76–80, 85, 140

Mapping, geologic, aid in, 11, 14–16, 166, 205, 210
 general, 2, 5, 111, 119, 174, 176, 177
 measurements with, 122–124
 with plane table, 92, 98, 105
Marker beds, 25, 51, 177, 179, 205
Marking units, 53–56, 67, 105, 106, 114, 208
Metamorphic rocks, described, 214–215
 listed, 5, 6, 16, 26, 47, 51, 186, 200, 208
Mining geology, 7

Nomograms, 71, 91, 133

Offset traverses, errors in, 177–179
 use of, 48, 54, 64, 67, 75, 121, 128, 142
Open-sight alidade, 92–95

Pacing, and compass traversing, 119–121, 132, 136–137, 140
 to measure distance, 81, 127, 129
Paulin altimeter, 106, 125–129, 132, 137, 167
Petroleum geology, 6, 7
Plane-tabling, described, 92–109
 errors with, 171, 172
 as field equipment, 45, 46, 68
 in general field use, 52–56, 110, 119, 163
 with other methods, 89, 130–133
 specific uses, 136–137, 140, 146, 148–151, 153, 154, 158, 160, 167
Porosity, 185, 187, 200–201
Precision of measurements, 2, 46, 133, 170–171
Profile sketches, 163, 186, 188, 206, 215

Ringer, George, 39, 40
Roundness of grains, 182, 187, 196–198, 206

Sampling rocks, for microscopic studies, 21, 24
 and plane-tabling, 98, 105–106
 procedure for, 53–56, 208–210
 sections for control of, 28–

30, 114, 124, 127, 180–182
  for subsurface studies, 10, 46–48, 51, 67
Sand-gauge, 196–197, 199
Sandstone classification, 189–190
Sorting of grains, 185, 187, 198–199
Stadia intercept, 81, 98–100
State geologic surveys, 3, 32, 33
Stratigraphic code, 16
Stratigraphy, 2–7, 214, 223
Strati-rule, 119
Subsurface studies, sections measured for, 2, 6–11, 208, 223
  units for, 51, 67, 68
Symbols, lithic, 219, 220

Telescopic alidade, errors with, 172
  as field equipment, 46, 68, 80
  measurements with, 70, 91, 110, 140, 150, 158
  with other methods, 84, 89, 132–133
  procedure with, 55, 92, 95–109
Telescopic hand level, 75, 80–84
Topographic expression of rocks, described, 40–43, 50, 205–206
  listing of, 17, 185, 187, 210, 211
  sketches of, 215, 218
Transit-tape method, described, 109–112
  errors with, 171, 172
  as field equipment, 45, 46, 52, 55
  with other methods, 132, 133
  specific uses, 136, 137, 140, 141, 152
Type sections, 16–18

United States Geological Survey, 3, 32–34, 214, 218

Volcanic rocks, described, 49, 52, 181, 189, 209–214
  measured sections of, 5–6, 27, 51, 122–123

Weathering of rocks, described, 36, 41, 50, 51, 204–205
  listed, 185, 187, 210–212, 214

Zigzag traverses, 144, 145, 160

Notes

Notes